THE WORLD OF 5G

Volume 5

INTELLIGENT MEDICINE

THE WORLD OF 5G
(In 5 Volumes)

5G的世界 — 万物互联
Originally published in Chinese by Guangdong Science and Technology Press Co., Ltd.
Copyright © Guangdong Science and Technology Press Co., Ltd. 2020

The World of 5G — Internet of Everything, Vol. 1
Copyright © 2022 by World Scientific Publishing Co. Pte. Ltd.

5G的世界 — 智能制造
Originally published in Chinese by Guangdong Science and Technology Press Co., Ltd.
Copyright © Guangdong Science and Technology Press Co., Ltd. 2020

The World of 5G — Intelligent Manufacturing, Vol. 2
Copyright © 2022 by World Scientific Publishing Co. Pte. Ltd.

5G的世界 — 智能家居
Originally published in Chinese by Guangdong Science and Technology Press Co., Ltd.
Copyright © Guangdong Science and Technology Press Co., Ltd. 2020

The World of 5G — Intelligent Home, Vol. 3
Copyright © 2022 by World Scientific Publishing Co. Pte. Ltd.

5G的世界 — 智慧交通
Originally published in Chinese by Guangdong Science and Technology Press Co., Ltd.
Copyright © Guangdong Science and Technology Press Co., Ltd. 2020

The World of 5G — Intelligent Transportation, Vol. 4
Copyright © 2022 by World Scientific Publishing Co. Pte. Ltd.

5G的世界 — 智慧医疗
Originally published in Chinese by Guangdong Science and Technology Press Co., Ltd.
Copyright © Guangdong Science and Technology Press Co., Ltd. 2020

The World of 5G — Intelligent Medicine, Vol. 5
Copyright © 2022 by World Scientific Publishing Co. Pte. Ltd.

THE WORLD OF 5G

Volume 5

INTELLIGENT MEDICINE

Wenhua Huang
Southern Medical University, China

Haibin Lin
Affiliated Hospital of Putian University, China

Translator
Straut Cao
Shenzhen Skyly Words Technology Co., Ltd.

Proofreader
Lianghe Dong
Mudanjiang Normal University, China

NEW JERSEY · LONDON · SINGAPORE · BEIJING · SHANGHAI · HONG KONG · TAIPEI · CHENNAI · TOKYO

Published by

World Scientific Publishing Co. Pte. Ltd.
5 Toh Tuck Link, Singapore 596224
USA office: 27 Warren Street, Suite 401-402, Hackensack, NJ 07601
UK office: 57 Shelton Street, Covent Garden, London WC2H 9HE

Library of Congress Cataloging-in-Publication Data
Names: Xue, Quan (Telecommunications professor), editor-in-chief.
Title: The world of 5G / authors, Quan Xue, South China University of Technology, China,
   Wenquan Che, South China University of Technology, China, Jishun Guo,
   Joyson Intelligent Automotive Research Institute, China, Wei Wu, Skyworth Group Co., Ltd., China,
   Zhiqiang Xu, Guangzhou Hantele Communication Co., Ltd., China, Wenhua Huang,
   Southern Medical University, China, Haibin Lin, Affiliated Hospital of Putian University, China.
Description: Singapore ; Hackensack, NJ : World Scientific Publishing Co. Pte. Ltd, [2022] |
   Includes bibliographical references and index. | Contents: v. 1. Internet of everything --
   v. 2. Intelligent manufacturing -- v. 3. Intelligent home -- v. 4. Intelligent transportation --
   v. 5. Intelligent medicine.
Identifiers: LCCN 2021061659 | ISBN 9789811250170 (set ; hardcover) | ISBN 9789811250187
   (set ; ebook for institutions) | ISBN 9789811250194 (set ; ebook for individuals) |
   ISBN 9789811244131 (v. 1 ; hardcover) | ISBN 9789811244148 (v. 1 ; ebook for institutions) |
   ISBN 9789811244155 (v. 1 ; ebook for individuals) | ISBN 9789811244223 (v. 2 ; hardcover) |
   ISBN 9789811244230 (v. 2 ; ebook for institutions) | ISBN 9789811244247 (v. 2 ; ebook for individuals) |
   ISBN 9789811244254 (v. 3 ; hardcover) | ISBN 9789811244261 (v. 3 ; ebook for institutions) |
   ISBN 9789811244278 (v. 3 ; ebook for individuals) | ISBN 9789811244162 (v. 4 ; hardcover) |
   ISBN 9789811244179 (v. 4 ; ebook for institutions | ISBN 9789811244186 (v. 4 ; ebook for individuals) |
   ISBN 9789811244193 (v. 5 ; hardcover) | ISBN 9789811244209 (v. 5 ; ebook for institutions) |
   ISBN 9789811244216 (v. 5 ; ebook for individuals)
Subjects: LCSH: 5G mobile communication systems. | Expert systems (Computer science) | Automation.
Classification: LCC TK5103.25 .X84 2022 | DDC 621.3845/6--dc23/eng/20220224
LC record available at https://lccn.loc.gov/2021061659

British Library Cataloguing-in-Publication Data
A catalogue record for this book is available from the British Library.

Copyright © 2022 by World Scientific Publishing Co. Pte. Ltd.

All rights reserved. This book, or parts thereof, may not be reproduced in any form or by any means, electronic or mechanical, including photocopying, recording or any information storage and retrieval system now known or to be invented, without written permission from the publisher.

For photocopying of material in this volume, please pay a copying fee through the Copyright Clearance Center, Inc., 222 Rosewood Drive, Danvers, MA 01923, USA. In this case permission to photocopy is not required from the publisher.

For any available supplementary material, please visit
https://www.worldscientific.com/worldscibooks/10.1142/12479#t=suppl

Printed in Singapore

Foreword
5G Empowers the Society for Development at a Rapid Speed

Being one of the buzzwords of the global media in recent years, 5G is very attractive because it carries great expectations from people, both in terms of the communication technology itself and the industry changes it could unleash. Recalling the development of human society, technological change is undoubtedly one of the biggest engines. Marked by the invention of the steam engine and electricity, the first two Industrial Revolutions featured mechanization and electrification, respectively. As the wheel of history rolls into the 21st century, a new round of Industrial Revolution featuring intelligence will be looming, and its impact on human civilization and economic development will be no less than that of the previous two Industrial Revolutions. But then what is pushing it? Compared with the previous two, the new Industrial Revolution is no longer pushed by a single technology but instead by the integration of multiple technologies, among which mobile communication, Internet, artificial intelligence, and biotechnology are the decisive elements.

5G, as the commanding heights of modern mobile technology, is an important engine that enables other key technologies mentioned above. Meanwhile, it can also be seen that 5G comes out when the new momentum is needed most by the Internet development. After almost linear rapid growth, the increment rate of China's Internet users is falling with the popularity rate of mobile phones almost refusing to grow. Owning to the fast pace of life, the netizens now pursue new forms of business with short periods, low investments, and quick returns. Faster speed and lower fees have mitigated the cost pressure on broadband Internet access when short videos and small programs are becoming popular. But these are still not enough to meet the requirements of the new format of the Internet. The future development of the Internet calls for new drivers and new models to solve this problem. The industrial Internet, regarded as the second half of the Internet, has just started, and its new driving forces cannot fill deficiencies of the consumer Internet driving force. At present, the Internet enters into a transition period of continuity for new drivers to replace the old ones. At a time when the consumption of the Internet needs to be intensified and the industrial Internet is starting to take off, 5G comes into being.

As the latest generation of cellular mobile communication technology, 5G is characterized by high speed, low latency, wide connectivity, and high reliability. Compared with 4G, 5G's peak rate increases by 30 times, user experience rate advances by 10 times, and spectrum efficiency accelerates by three times. Moreover, compared to 4G, 5G mobile supports high-speed rail with the speed of 500 km/h, with its wireless interface delay reduced by 90%, the connection density enhanced by 10 times, energy efficiency and traffic density improved by 100 times, enough to support the mobile Internet industry and many applications of the Internet. Compared with the previous four generations of mobile communication technologies, the most important change in 5G is the shift from individual-oriented use to industry-oriented applications, providing indispensable high-speed, massive, and low-latency connectivity for Internet of Everything needed by the new round of Industrial Revolution. Therefore, 5G is not only merely a communication technology but also an important "infrastructure".

It is well timed and also quite accountable in cultural inheritance for Guangdong Science and Technology Publishing House to take the lead in organizing the compilation and distribution of this book series and to popularize 5G knowledge in the society for improving the national scientific literacy when the whole society is talking about 5G with great expectations. Compared with the numerous books about 5G in the market, this series stands out with its own characteristics. First of all, Professor Xue Quan, the Chief Editor, who has been focusing on the research of 5G cutting-edge core technologies in recent years, is an expert in the fields of millimeter wave and terahertz. He took the lead in the compilation of this series with his team responsible for the volume, *5G Internet of*

Everything, thus aiming to well leverage the tool for the popularization of science to present 5G technology mass-orientally. In addition, with the focus on the integration and application of 5G in the vertical industry, the series comes out just in line with the close social concerns about 5G. The team included industry experts from the Guangdong Provincial Key Laboratory of Millimeter Wave and Terahertz in the South China University of Technology, Automotive Engineering Research Institute of Guangzhou Automobile Group Co., Ltd., Southern Medical University, Guangzhou Hanxin Communication Technology Co., Ltd., Skyworth Group Co., Ltd., for the corresponding volume, respectively. This book series is targeted at the current pain points of the industry, yet contributes to an unfettered imagination of the future of the 5G-enabling industry. It will be an invaluable science book for the public yearning for new technology for a new round of industrial transformation. The first issue of the book series consists of five volumes.

What's remarkable is that while the book focuses on how 5G will revolutionize the vertical industry if integrated with other technologies, it also explores the possible negative effects of technological advances on human beings. In the progress of science and technology, it is essential to stick to human nature, ethics, morality, and law. So the acceleration of the development of science and technology, with "safety valve" and "brake" being indispensable, shouldn't be based on the sacrifice of the dominance of human nature and the thinking ability of human beings. We need to think of science and technology as a "double-edged sword" and better exploit the advantages and avoid disadvantages while turning the passive reaction into an active response.

Coming in with a roar, 5G will have an immeasurable impact on the development of human society. Let's work together and march toward the future.

Wu Hequan
Member of Chinese Academy of Engineering

Foreword
5G as the Engine for Upgrading and Development of the Vertical Industries

As we all know, we are gradually entering a digital era, and many industries and technologies will progress around the data chain, in which the main effect of mobile communication technology is data transmission. Applications that require performance such as high-definition video, multi-device access, and real-time two-way interaction between multiple people are difficult to achieve without the support of high-speed communication technology. As the latest generation of cellular mobile communication technology, 5G features high speed, low delay, wide connection, and high reliability.

The year 2020 marks the first year for 5G commercial use and then the employment of 5G is expected to peak around 2035. 5G will be mainly applied in the following seven fields: smart creation, smart city, smart grid, smart office, smart security, telemedicine and health care, and commercial retail. In these seven fields, it is estimated that nearly 50% of 5G components will be applied to smart creation, while nearly 18.7% will be applied to smart city construction.

The importance of 5G is not only reflected in its great promotion of upgrading industries such as smart creation but also reflected in its direct correlation with the development of artificial intelligence. The development of artificial intelligence requires a large number of user cases and data, and the amount of data that 4G Internet of Things (IoT) can provide for learning is incomparable to that of 5G. Therefore, the development of

5G IoT plays a very important role in promoting the development of artificial intelligence. Relying on 5G can help promote the upgrading of many vertical industries. It is also for this reason that 5G's leading development has become an important engine to promote the development of national science and technology and economy and has also become the focus of competition between China and the United States in the field of science and technology.

Against this background, Guangdong Science and Technology Publishing House took the lead in organizing the compilation and distribution of the "5G World" book series, with the focus on the integrated application and empowerment of 5G in many industries, including manufacturing, medical care, transportation, home furniture, finance, education, and so on. On the one hand, it is a courageous and culturally responsible measure to popularize 5G among the public, enhancing national scientific literacy. On the other hand, this book is also an utterly precious reference for industry insiders who want to understand the trend for the development of 5G technology and industrial integration.

This book series was done under the guidance of Chief Editor, Professor Xue Quan, the Director of the Guangdong Key Laboratory of Millimeter Wave and Terahertz, South China University of Technology. As an expert in the fields of millimeter wave and terahertz technology, Professor Xue Quan will manage to make a book series of popular science with accurate and natural technical features. This book series is scheduled to be publish the first editions of five volumes, including *The World of 5G: Internet of Everything, The World of 5G: Intelligent Manufacturing, The World of 5G: Intelligent Home, The World of 5G: Intelligent Transportation,* and *The World of 5G: Intelligent Medicine.* The compilation team of this series boasts of strong support. In addition to *The World of 5G: Internet of Everything*, which was written by the technical team of Guangdong Millimeter Wave and Terahertz Key Laboratory of South China University of Technology, the other four volumes were mainly written by relevant industry experts. Among all the volumes, *The World of 5G: Intelligent Manufacturing* was written by experts from the Auto Engineering Research Institute of Guangzhou Automobile Group Co., Ltd., while *The World of 5G: Intelligent Medicine* was written by experts from Southern Medical University. *The World of 5G: Intelligent Transportation* was written by Guangzhou Hantele Communication Co., Ltd., and *The World of 5G: Intelligent Home* was written by Skyworth Group Co., Ltd. This kind of cross-industry combination writing team possesses a strong complementary and professional system for the following reasons: for one thing, technical experts can fully grasp the evolution of mobile communication technology and key technologies of 5G; for another, industry experts can accurately feel the pain points of the industry as well as analyze the advantages and challenges of the industries integrated with 5G through incise writing around the central themes to provide a valuable reference for industry peers with real and vivid cases.

Besides a vivid description of the huge changes that could be brought about by the 5G technology merged into industries, what makes this book novel and fresh is the fact that they also discuss the negative effects the rapid advance of technology may have on human beings. The rapid development of high technology should not be done at the cost of human nature, ethics, and thoughts. It is necessary to make sure that technology conforms to science and ethics with the essential "cushion" and "safety valve".

Mao Junfa
Member of Chinese Academy of Sciences

Preface

As a revolutionary leap in technology, 5G provides Internet of Everything with important technical support. Furthermore, it will bring prosperity for mobile Internet and industrial Internet and provide many industries with unprecedented opportunities, thus being expected to trigger profound changes in the whole society. What is 5G? How will 5G empower various industries and promote a new round of Industrial Revolution? The answers can be found in the series *The World of 5G*, which consists of five volumes.

    The volume *The World of 5G: Internet of Everything* is edited by Xue Quan, Director of Guangdong Key Laboratory of Millimeter Wave and Terahertz, South China University of Technology, and mainly expounds the iterative development history of mobile communication technology, the characteristics and limitations of the first four generations of mobile communication technology, the technical characteristics of 5G and its possible industrial application prospects, and the development trend of mobile communication technology in the post-5G era. By reading this volume, the reader can obtain a carefully and skillfully drawn picture of the past, present, and future applications of 5G.

    The volume *The World of 5G: Intelligent Manufacturing* is edited by Dr. Guo Jishun of Automotive Engineering Research Institute of Guangzhou Automobile Group Co., Ltd., and mainly introduces the development process of the Industrial Revolution, the opportunity brought about by 5G to the manufacturing industry, the upgrade of smart creation assisted by 5G, and the application of intelligent production based on 5G. Through this volume, readers can understand the opportunities for the transformation of traditional manufacturing produced by 5G+ smart creation and learn by experience what kind of revolution manufacturing innovation will create in the society.

The volume *The World of 5G: Intelligent Home* is edited by Wu Wei from Skyworth Group Co., Ltd., and mainly elaborates on the evolution of smart home, the key technologies that 5G uses to facilitate the intelligent development of home life, as well as innovative smart home products based on 5G technology. Home furnishing is closely tied to our daily life. By reading this volume, readers can understand the convenience and comfort arising from the integration of 5G and smart home. It provides a glimpse of the wonderful life that technology has created.

The volume *The World of 5G: Intelligent Transportation* is edited by Xu Zhiqiang from Guangzhou Hexin Communications Technology Co., Ltd., and mainly describes the development process of smart transportation, the key 5G technologies and architectures used in smart transportation, as well as the application examples of smart transportation based on 5G. By reading this volume, readers can be fully informed about the future development trend of smart transportation led by 5G technology.

The volume *The Word of 5G: Intelligent Medicine* is edited by Huang Wenhua and Lin Haibin from Southern Medical University, and mainly focuses on the effect of the integration of 5G and medical treatment, including the advantages of smart medicine compared with traditional medical treatment, how 5G promotes the development of smart medicine and smart medicine terminals and new medical applications integrated with 5G. Reading between the lines, readers can gain a comprehensive understanding of the huge application potential of 5G technology in the medical industry and be keenly aware of the well-being that technological progress has contributed to human health.

Finally, we specially acknowledge the funding from projects such as prior research and development projects "Key Technology of Millimeter Wave Integrated RF Front-end System Compatible with C Band (2018YFB1802000)" of the National Ministry of Science and Technology, the major science and technology project of "Research on 5G Millimeter Wave Broadband High Efficiency Chip and Phased Array System (2018B010115001)" of Guangdong Science and Technology Department, and Strategic Consulting Project of "Guangdong New Generation Information Technology Development Strategy Research (201816611292)" of Guangdong Research Institute of Chinese Academy of Engineering Development Strategy.

5G brings us technological change, industry upgrade, and social upheaval with unprecedented speed and strength, while also generating great challenges. Let's navigate our way ahead while harnessing the waves of 5G.

About the Authors

 **Haibin Lin** is Professor, Chief Physician, Doctoral Supervisor, and President of National Hospital, who has also been offered the State Council special government allowance. He is the Chair of Orthopedics Department of Taiwan Medical Association of Cross-strait Medical and Health Exchange Association, and the Member of the Chinese Department of International Orthopedics and Trauma Surgery Department, Chinese Medical Association, Chinese Medical Doctors Association, Chinese Rehabilitation Medical Association, and other professional groups of academic organizations. He is also Deputy Chairman of Fujian Orthopedics Branch, Microsurgery Branch, Repair and Reconstruction Committee.

Professor Lin has been engaged in clinical medicine, teaching, and scientific research for more than 30 years, and is committed to promoting the development of orthopedics, especially minimally invasive spine surgery. He has conducted in-depth research on spinal surgery, joint surgery, reduction and internal fixation of complex fractures, and is particularly good at the innovation and application of minimally invasive surgery theory in spinal surgery.

 **Wenhua Huang** is Professor and PhD Supervisor of Southern Medical University, MD, successor of Academician Shizhen Zhong. He is also the winner of the first "China Young Anatomical Scientist Award", Academic Leader of National Key Discipline of Human Anatomy, Director of Guangdong Key Laboratory on Medical Biomechanics, Chairman of the Professional Committee on Basic Microscopic Research of Chinese Medical Doctor Association Microsurgeons Branch, Deputy Director of the Chinese Division of Digital Orthopedics Society of SICOT, and Deputy Director of The Chinese Clinical Anatomy Committee.

Professor Huang Mainly engages in the clinical applied anatomy, digital medicine, and medical 3D printing research. He has presided and participated in plenty of projects including the National Key Research and Development Program, Special Project for Major Instruments of National Natural Science Foundation, General Project of National Natural Science Foundation, National 863 Program and so on. He has established a high-level scientific research technology platform represented by the Clinical Applied Anatomy, Digital Medicine, and 3D Printing Technology together with Academician Shizhen Zhong. He has published 371 scientific research papers in domestic and international journals, including 136 SCI entries and 67 patents applied. He has cultivated more than 130 Master's/PhD students and postdoctoral researchers. He is committed to basic anatomical research and clinical translational application. He has won eight national and provincial Science and Technology Progress Awards.

Contents

Foreword: 5G Empowers the Society for Development at a Rapid Speed	v
Foreword: 5G as the Engine for Upgrading and Development of the Vertical Industries	ix
Preface	xiii
About the Authors	xvii

Chapter 1 Intelligent Medicine: The Magic Power for Healing the Wounded and Rescue of the Dying   **1**

1.1 Little "Thorns" on the Traditional Road of Seeking Medical Services   1
     1.1.1 Some patients' difficulties in seeking medical services   1
     1.1.2 Uneven distribution of medical resources   5
     1.1.3 Difficulties in closing the loop of the online and the offline medical services   7
     1.1.4 Poor doctor–patient communication and coordination   8
1.2 Science and Technology for Intelligent Medicine   10
     1.2.1 The history and development of WIT120   11
     1.2.2 Structural system of WIT120   16
     1.2.3 Composition of WIT120   21
     1.2.4 Application of WIT120   24

xx   The World of 5G: Intelligent Medicine

**Chapter 2 Making Distant Diagnosis and Treatment
           Possible with 5G**   **31**
2.1 Seeing Doctors with 5G Network at Your Side   32
     2.1.1 5G outpatient service — National experts
            at your side   32
     2.1.2 5G brainstorming — Seeing a doctor who
            is a thousand miles away   34
     2.1.3 5G quick wits — Strategize wisely   39
     2.1.4 5G cloud medical records — Easy access
            to medical information   41
2.2 Customized New Health Manager for You   46
     2.2.1 Personalized medical care   46
     2.2.2 Management of personal health records   49
     2.2.3 Remote monitoring   53
     2.2.4 Benefits for the disabled   57

Chapter 3 Better Healthcare within Your Reach   **61**
3.1 Intelligent Terminals Supported by 5G Technology   61
     3.1.1 Smart watches and smart bracelets   62
     3.1.2 Intelligent medicine box   65
     3.1.3 Intelligent blood pressure monitor   67
     3.1.4 Ambulance   67
3.2 AR/VR Applications Driven by 5G   69
     3.2.1 Virtual teaching platform based on augmented
            reality (AR)/virtual reality (VR)   70
     3.2.2 VR ward visits   73
3.3 5G+ AI Diagnosis: 5G Can Meet Your Urgent Needs   74
     3.3.1 Intelligent diagnosis of skin diseases   74
     3.3.2 AI can diagnose eye diseases   76
     3.3.3 Accurate analysis of brain diseases   78

Chapter 4 5G-Pioneered Robust Healthcare for the Future   **81**
4.1 Easy Access to Famous Doctors at Any Time   81
     4.1.1 Holographic projection: A new mode of
            medical interaction   81
     4.1.2 Famous doctors gather and Big Data helps you
            diagnose the disease   85
4.2 Complex Operation Can be Simply Done   89
     4.2.1 By utilizing AR/VR technology, full view without
            dead angle can be realized   89

      4.2.2 Machine intelligence: "Iron and steel" doctor
           would serve you wholeheartedly   93
  4.3 Relevant Laws and Regulations   96
      4.3.1 Will privacy breaches happen in medical data?   96
      4.3.2 Who is responsible for WIT120?   100

Bibliography   105

Index   109

Chapter 1

Intelligent Medicine: The Magic Power for Healing the Wounded and Rescue of the Dying

1.1 Little "Thorns" on the Traditional Road of Seeking Medical Services

Since the reform and opening up, China has made remarkable achievements in its social and economic development, and the medical and healthcare industry has also stepped up to a new level. However, the current public health services available in the society, irrespective of whether it is in terms of quantity or quality, cannot meet the overall needs of the people, though the material conditions are highly developed, with people's living standards constantly improved and people's awareness of health constantly strengthened. The unreasonable allocation of medical resources, the concentration of high-quality medical resources in large cities and hospitals, and the low level of grassroots medical care make the social problem of "difficulties and high expenses in getting medical services" prominent.

1.1.1 *Some patients' difficulties in seeking medical services*

As the saying goes, "Sickness is normal for all mortals". To solve the problem of "difficulties and high expenses in getting medical services", we need to give full consideration to its causes. The core problem of

2 The World of 5G: Intelligent Medicine

Figure 1.1 "Difficulties in getting medical services" and "high expenses of getting medical services".

"difficulties in getting medical services" is the contradiction between supply and demand, which is the reality China has to face for the insufficient total medical and health resources and the unreasonable healthcare structure. Of course, the "difficulties in getting medical services" are not evenly distributed but mainly witnessed in seeking medical services from affiliated hospitals of famous universities in big cities, such as Beijing, Shanghai, and Guangzhou (Fig. 1.1).

It's 4 a.m., but more than 1,000 people have been queuing outside a hospital in Beijing, many of whom starting queuing at midnight. During the peak flu season, many parents are sitting on folding stools waiting for registration at a hospital in Tianjin. Some parents started waiting in line at the hospital from 12 p.m. despite the fact that the outpatient service would not start registration until 4:30 p.m. The scenes at these two hospitals are just a microcosm of what happens in all grade-A class-three hospitals in big cities. "3 hours in queuing for 3 minutes medical checkup" and "difficulties in registration and hospitalization while seeing a doctor" have made all the patients and their families miserable.

The game among the government, hospitals, patients, and "appointment scalpers" is repeatedly on show every day in major hospitals, due to the "difficulties of registration" in well-known major hospitals (Fig. 1.2) and difficulties in making appointments with famous experts have become

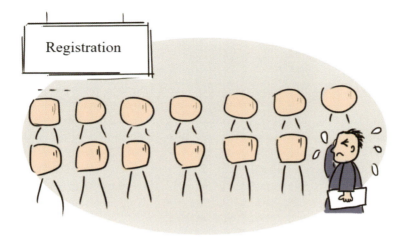

Figure 1.2 Difficulties of registration.

Figure 1.3 Appointment scalpers sell appointments at a high price.

a common social phenomenon, which was even worsened by the resulting "appointment scalpers" (Fig. 1.3).

"Difficulties of getting medical services" is reflected in choosing the right hospital and in the huge time cost in seeking medical attention.

4 *The World of 5G: Intelligent Medicine*

People would waste a lot of time and energy in their confusion, trying to figure out the correct procedure at the hospitals of numerous departments for various checkups at different sections. The results from relevant media surveys show that the average time consumed for Chinese patients' visit to the hospital is about three hours, with more than 75% of it spent on registration, payment, waiting for clinical reception, and queuing for examination, but just less than 10 minutes averagely on the communication between the patients and the attending physicians during the diagnosis (Fig. 1.4).

The aging of the population and the turning of the disease spectrum toward chronicity have increased the difficulties and expenses of treatment. According to the United Nations, the country or region with more than 10% of its population over the age of 60 should be considered as an aging society. According to China's fifth population census in 2000, the population above the age of 60 is 130 million, accounting for 10.2% of the

Figure 1.4   Tension in the doctor–patient relationship.

total population, which is proof that China has entered an aging society. The average prevalence rate and duration of illness in the elderly are two to three times higher than in the general population. In China, the elderly occupies about 80% of the medical and health resources, of which 80% are used for elderly patients with acute and serious diseases. However, it is still difficult for the elderly to see a doctor, mainly due to the inconvenience in traveling, the long journey to the hospitals, and the complicated procedures of seeing a doctor.

1.1.2 *Uneven distribution of medical resources*

As the main body of the medical service industry, medical and health institutions are divided into three categories in China: hospitals, community health service centers, and township health centers. The number of these three types of medical and health institutions has been steadily increasing year by year, with the total number of medical and health institutions in China being over one million in 2018. Even so, in the context of an aging population, the total amount of medical and health resources in China is still seriously insufficient, considering the social and economic development and the people's increasing demand for medical services (Fig. 1.5).

China's population accounts for 22% of the world's population, while its medical resources account for only 2% of that of the world.

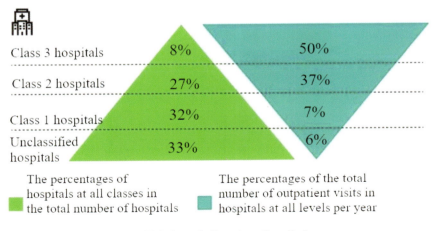

Figure 1.5 Unbalanced allocation of medical resources.

6 *The World of 5G: Intelligent Medicine*

On average, one doctor has to serve 1,000 patients. Take Peking Union Medical College Hospital as an example. Compared to the Mayo Clinic in the United States, the Peking Union Medical College Hospital employs more than 4,000 people and receives about 2.26 million medical consultations every year. While the Mayo Clinic employs more than 60,000 people, 15 times more than that of the Union Hospital, and receives about 1.16 million patients annually, only half of that of the Peking Union Medical College Hospital.

The total amount of medical resources is insufficient, the distribution is unbalanced (Fig. 1.6), the shortage of medical staff is huge, and the health development lags behind the economic development. These are the main problems in the development of medical and health services in China. With 80% of China's medical resources concentrated in cities and about 80% of the medical resources in cities concentrated in major hospitals, the lack of medical services and medicines in rural areas and remote areas is prominent, and patients in urban and rural areas often need to travel long distances to seek medical treatment in other places like hospitals of higher levels. Medical resources of hospitals in central urban regions are occupied by patients with minor and common diseases, which also explains the "difficulties and high expenses of getting medical services" after waiting for a long time.

Figure 1.6 Uneven distribution of medical resources.

Improving the healthcare system, especially promoting the coverage of medical services, is a top priority in the government's 13th Five-Year Plan. The social problems caused by the imbalance of the medical and health system and the aging of the population can be solved by scientific and technological means, and the scientific and technological medical plan represented by digital medicine serves as the most feasible way to alleviate the problem of "difficulties in getting medical services". The *Opinions of the General Office of the State Council on Promoting the Development of "Internet plus Medical Health"* issued in April 2018 shows that the country attaches great importance to the cause of telemedicare. Alvin Toffler, an American futurist, once predicted, "In future medical activities, doctors will diagnose and treat patients according to various information of patients from afar displayed on the screen". This prediction is coming true.

1.1.3 *Difficulties in closing the loop of the online and the offline medical services*

With the continuous development of China's mobile communication and Internet+, Internet medical services, which offer various forms of medical and health management services such as health education, medical data query, online disease consultation, remote consultation, remote treatment, and rehabilitation with the Internet as the carrier has risen in response to the proper time and conditions. In recent years, China has also seen some progress in Internet medical services when the Internet medical services in developed countries led by the United States have become relatively mature. Medical apps, namely, medical applications based on mobile terminals, have sprung up like mushrooms on the Internet, providing services such as seeking medical services, appointment and registration, and information inquiry. According to iResearch, there are already more than 2,000 mobile medical apps in China.

Although initial achievements have been made in the development of Internet medical services, we must remain cool-headed and remember that there are still insufficiencies in hardware and software in the development of Internet medical services, which hindered the information connectivity and the sharing of resources. Medical treatment through clicks, like water without a source or a tree without roots, still calls for further diagnosis and treatment from hospitals of bricks to improve the health of the patients.

Internet medical treatment does not increase medical resources, but works through the optimization and integration effect of the Internet to integrate and utilize the existing medical resources so as to improve the efficiency of medical resources and alleviate the problems caused by the uneven distribution of medical resources. Currently, Internet medical services mostly stop at patients' online consultation to obtain targeted treatment plans before receiving treatment in offline physical hospitals.

The ultimate goal of Internet medical services should be to build an integrated online and offline comprehensive health service platform to provide the public with comprehensive and whole-process autonomous integrated health services, which not only serve the patients and their families but also the doctors, nurses, hospitals, and the government. The comprehensive health service platform can not only help patients by providing abundant information about the characteristics and levels of hospitals and experts but also provide online studios for doctors and nurses to carry out multi-site practice. Unfortunately, the combination of online and offline medical services is not well integrated and these do not cooperate well with each other to offer closed-loop services.

Internet medical treatment met its bottleneck at closing the loop of medical services both online and offline, at a time when the space–time limitation of medical treatment has been gradually broken with the development of mobile Internet, nanotechnology, and sensing technology. Doctors always remain the core of the diagnosis and treatment system. But regarding the lag of Internet medical treatment, on the one hand, doctors are largely restricted by the management system of hospitals as they are employed by certain hospitals, and on the other hand, experts at big hospitals, overwhelmed by floods of patients, have neither the time nor the incentive to make an online diagnosis. How Internet medical enterprises can form a community of interests with doctors and how they can achieve the reasonable allocation of resources of doctors will determine the development direction of the industry.

1.1.4 *Poor doctor–patient communication and coordination*

Doctor–patient communication, as a very important part of medical services, is closely related to the quality of medical services. Improving doctor–patient communication has become crucial to improving the management and control system for medical quality, with the patients'

Intelligent Medicine 9

demands on the quality of medical services within the society progressing fast, the construction of the health legal system constantly improving, people's life continuously enhancing, and the consciousness of rights increasing day by day.

Tension between doctors and patients contributes to about 70% of the reasons for increased medical disputes caused by poor communication between doctors and patients (Fig. 1.7). Doctor–patient communication refers to the communication between the doctor (and/or hospital) and the patient (and/or the patient's family members), which mainly aims at the cooperation between the doctors and the patients to cure injuries and diseases for improving the health of the patients. Doctor–patient communication can have shared benefits between each other by developing their relationship.

"Seeing a doctor is not like buying things", said Zhong Nanshan, an academician of the Chinese Academy of Engineering. "The communication between doctors and patients is very important. The less communication there is, the more problems there will be".

Poor doctor–patient communication is mainly caused by the following: (1) medical staff talking and acting according to outdated standards in their medical services which are way behind; (2) the cold attitude of medical staff while communicating with patients; (3) lack of attention to

Figure 1.7 Poor doctor–patient communication.

the concerned crowd due to inadequate awareness about active prevention and failure in giving a proper response to problems that arise; (4) uneven distribution of limited medical resources which is reflected in the serious shortage of medical staff and hospital beds and means for communication; (5) patients' distrust in the medical staff or even the medical industry; (6) dissatisfaction of the patients and their families, who are poorly equipped with the knowledge of medicine, when their expectations for medical services received, usually higher than it should be, are not met; (7) contradiction between doctors and patients deliberately simulated by some of the patients of ill nature in the process of seeking medical services, on the purpose of escaping medical expenses, or even improper benefits through blackmailing the medical staff.

Good doctor–patient communication, which requires the joint cooperation and efforts of the society, the medical staff, and the patients, can promote the healthy development of the doctor–patient relationship. The new medical reform has introduced new ideas and new ways of thinking to both doctors and patients, and also put forward new requirements for medical work. The efficiency of medical work can be greatly improved through high-tech means like the Internet, which can maximize the effect of limited medical resources and ease the contradiction between doctors and patients.

Hippocrates, the father of medicine, had once said, "It is more important to understand the patients than to know their illness". Therefore, it is necessary to build a great communication mechanism which integrates doctor–patient communication into the medical culture, management system, and team training so as to create a great communication mechanism to include old patients, present patients, and future patients through innovative communication methods based on the application of mobile communication and Internet technologies, professional communication skills, and enhanced communication mechanisms (Fig. 1.8).

1.2 Science and Technology for Intelligent Medicine

In 2009, International Business Machines Corporation (IBM) put forward the concept of Wise Information Technology of 120 (WIT120) for the first time in the strategy of "smarter planet" for a "patient-centered" medical service system to realize the informational interaction among medical personnel, medical institutions, medical equipment, patients, and their

Intelligent Medicine 11

Figure 1.8 The foundation of a good doctor–patient relationship.

families through the connection between advanced technologies of mobile communication, Internet and Internet of Things (IoT), people, information, equipment, and other resources in the healthcare system. A patient-centered medical data network has gradually come into being, thanks to the rapid development of the Internet of Things, mobile Internet, Big Data, cloud platform, nanotechnology, sensors, and other technologies, especially the emergence of 5G mobile communication technology, which has greatly promoted the integration of artificial intelligence and medical services. With the development of 5G mobile Internet, WIT120 will usher in a period of explosive growth.

1.2.1 *The history and development of WIT120*

1.2.1.1 *The origin and development of WIT120*

WIT120, short for Wise Information Technology of 120, is a medical term emerging in recent years, which defines a mode of medical service that realizes information-based interaction among medical staff, medical institutions, medical equipment, patients, and their families through a regional medical information platform for health records with patient data as the center based on advanced technologies like mobile communication and Internet of Things.

Outline for the Planning of the National Medical and Health Service System (2015–2020) promulgated in China in 2015 put forward that the project of cloud service for Health China should be carried out, using new technologies such as mobile Internet, Internet of Things, cloud computing, and wearable devices, to promote the health information services and the WIT120 services for the benefit of all the people. Besides, the application of health Big Data should be promoted to change the service pattern for improving the service and management gradually.

WIT120 combines new sensors, Internet of Things, cloud computing, mobile communication, and other technologies with modern medical concepts, builds a regional medical information platform centered on electronic health records, integrates the internal business processes of hospitals, and optimizes regional medical resources. It can provide the patients with fast and convenient online appointments and two-way referral between medical institutions, simplify processes, reduce multifarious formalities for the patient, and reasonably assign the medical resources to each patient, truly taking patients as the center. In the future, more new technologies such as artificial intelligence and sensing technology will be applied in the medical industry to promote the healthy and rapid development of the medical industry by making the medical service system truly intelligent. Under the background of China's new medical reform, WIT120 has entered the life of people, providing convenient and efficient medical services for patients (Fig. 1.9).

1.2.1.2 *The composition of WIT120*

The WIT120 system is composed of the smart hospital system, the regional health system, and the family health system. The smart hospital system includes the digital hospital and promoted applications, among which the digital hospital includes five parts, namely, the hospital information system, the laboratory information management system, the storage system for information about medical images, the medical information transmission system, and the doctors' workstation. Promoted applications include technologies like remote image transmission, computation, and processing of massive data. The digital hospital and promoted applications supplement each other, which improves the medical service.

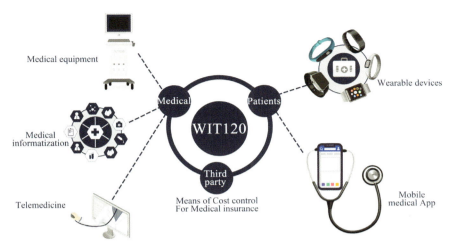

Figure 1.9 Structure diagram of WIT120.

The regional health system, consisting of two parts, namely, the regional health platform and the public health system, aims to realize the sharing of information and resources between patients and medical institutions at all levels through cutting-edge science and computer technology, so as to solve the difficulties in seeking medical services for patients. The family health system is aimed at people having difficulties in getting about and those with chronic diseases. It enables their doctors to intelligently monitor their conditions at home so that they can receive real-time effective medical assistance. The three components of WIT120 perform their respective functions and are closely linked, providing technical support and systematic management for WIT120.

1.2.1.3 *The characteristics and advantages of WIT120*

Compared to the traditional medical service, WIT120, which combines modern medicine and information technology, has new characteristics. These can be described as follows:

(1) *Interconnected*: Doctors can monitor patients' conditions anytime and anywhere through mobile terminals to make real-time changes in the treatment, and patients can make independent choices about the doctors or hospitals.

(2) *Collaborative*: A comprehensive and professional medical network can be established in the shared integrated information database for the medical staff to check up on the diagnosis and treatment information of the patients in real time through the Internet.
(3) *Preventable*: Quick and effective response can be realized through real-time analysis during major medical events.
(4) *Universality*: The WIT120 system covers large, medium, and small hospitals in an all-round way and supports the seamless connection between township and community hospitals and central hospitals, so that the medical staff of township and community hospitals can promptly obtain expert diagnosis and treatment advice, arrange patient referral, and receive medical training.
(5) *Innovation*: The theoretical and clinical treatment capacity will be enhanced and further promote clinical innovation and research.
(6) *Reliability*: It can enable practitioners to support their diagnosis with adequate scientific evidence obtained from the system, such as the mobile medical library.

The mode of WIT120 is making the whole process, from the beginning of patients' perception of physical discomfort to the targeted treatment by doctors, intelligent, informationized, and accurate. With the patient-centered service concept as the central idea of intelligent medicine, the application of technologies such as medical Big Data, cloud computing, and 5G communication enables convenient, fast, prompt, and targeted medical services for the patients. WIT120 enables more accurate and efficient communication between patients and medical workers, with information sharing as a key link for improved medical services by equipping the doctors with the diagnosis and treatment information about the patients promptly from the shared database.

1.2.1.4 *The application of WIT120*

Applications of smart outpatient service, smart ward, smart health management, and mobile medical library cover the whole process of diagnosis and treatment and enable the one-stop medical service for the patients (Fig. 1.10). The smart outpatient service implements multi-channel appointment for registration and scheduled appointments. It adopts "payment after treatment", in which the payment can be put off until after completing the procedures of registration, medical treatment, testing, and

Intelligent Medicine 15

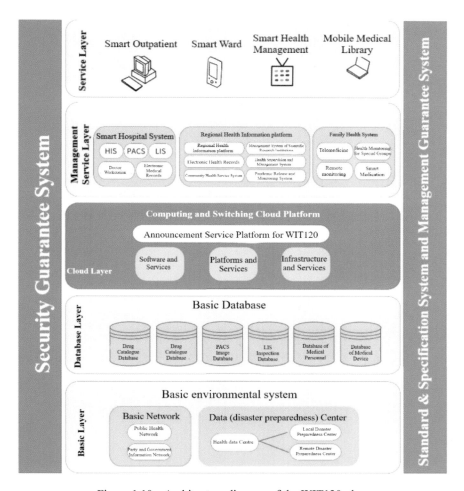

Figure 1.10 Architecture diagram of the WIT120 plan.

taking medicine. A variety of online and offline payment methods are supported, enabling the means to pay the fees for the diagnosis and treatment laboratory test through the self-service terminals.

The smart ward can provide the patient with the whole-process automated services, during which patients can finish a series of hospitalization and discharge procedures through self-service. The information construction with electronic medical records at the core of it realized information integration among medical images, medical inspection, and electronic medical records. Medical workers can get the diagnosis and treatment information about the patients promptly, so as to carry out mobile rounds and mobile nursing and help realize a new management mode for medical treatment and nursing. The smart health management comprehensively records the patient's health condition and diagnosis and treatment information and offers relevant information like records of outpatient service, hospitalization, medication history, treatment effect, cost list, examination sheet, inspection sheet, report card, and online consultation on the mobile terminals where one can also check their health status in a timely manner on the mobile terminals and constantly monitor it by consulting with a 24-hour online doctor, with the attitude of "self-examination of physical discomfort, inquiring for minor illness first, and going to hospital for serious illness" permeated into the concept of WIT120. The mobile medical library enables every medical worker to consult the drug bank, disease bank, symptom bank, and clinical case analysis of authoritative medical dictionaries on the mobile terminal anytime and anywhere, and even to consult relevant literature in medical journals at any time.

1.2.2 Structural system of WIT120

The structural system of WIT120 includes the industrial chain, system architecture, and technical architecture, which will be described in detail in the following sections.

1.2.2.1 Industry chain

The industry chain of WIT120 includes hospitals, patients, and third parties (Fig. 1.11).

WIT120 mainly benefits the hospitals with intelligent medical equipment, medical informationization, and telemedicine, among which the medical informationization refers to the digitalization, networking, and informationization of medical services that integrate computer science, modern network communication technology, and database technology to carry out the collection, storage, processing, extraction, and data exchange of patient information and management information between hospitals and departments under the hospital. Telemedicine uses new technologies such as mobile communication, Internet of Things, cloud computing, and Articulated Naturality Web to realize telemedicine operation, and many intelligent health and medical products are gradually developed by merchants.

Intelligent Medicine 17

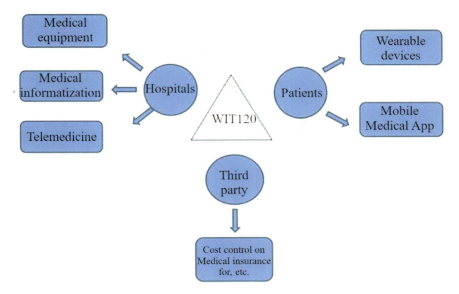

Figure 1.11 The industry chain of WIT120.

Intelligent wearable devices and mobile medical apps have been developed for patients. Being portable, wearable devices can provide real-time monitoring for different patients, which facilitates the connection between patients and hospitals, and enables patients to avoid hospitalization for minor diseases and get timely treatment for serious ones. This technology will greatly reduce the hospitalization and consultation rates of patients. Medical apps based on mobile terminals mainly provide patients with services like online consultation, appointment registration, drug procurement, and professional information query.

The third party, which is independent of the patient and the doctor, can help greatly reduce the conflict of interest between patients and medical workers by the rational use and efficient operation of the medical insurance fund through the intelligent control of medical insurance expenditure by means of informatization.

1.2.2.2 *System architecture*

The system architecture of WIT120 includes the application support cloud platform, the infrastructure layer, the standard and specification system, and the security guarantee system. The application support cloud platform mainly includes the public access platform for WIT120, a user-centered integrated health service system for residents with the aim to provide patients with services such as personalized health counseling and self-health management after monitoring and evaluating the health of the residents, the development of the diseases, and the whole process of rehabilitation treatment. Of course, residents can enjoy easy access to personal health information, such as personal electronic health records and electronic medical records, on their mobile terminals at anytime and anywhere as well as other personalized services such as medication reminders on the terminals.

The application support cloud platform is composed of the service platform layer and the basic support system, and the service platform layer can be further divided into the smart cloud service platform and the smart cloud data center. The smart cloud service platform, as a kind of integrated platform, is mainly responsible for carrying out the data collection, exchange, and integration of medical institutions, so as to offer the smart cloud service with "residents health records as the core, electronic medical records as the basis, chronic disease prevention and treatment as the focus, and decision analysis as the guarantee" through the unified basic services. The cloud service platform is used to provide medical data among hospitals and build a WIT120 data center. The smart cloud data center can provide strong data support for medical decision makers through its collection of diagnosis and treatment data of various medical institutions and its ability in performing further analysis of the data.

The basic support system, consisting of the operation support platform and the basic equipment, the two major components of the basic support system, provides software and hardware support for the cloud service platform, among which the operation support platform is composed of basic middleware and operation support service. The basic middleware includes resource virtualization middleware, application service middleware, and database middleware. The operation support service can efficiently analyze and process massive amounts of data as well as realize the organic integration of infrastructure. With the functions of cloud computing and cloud storage, it can solve the problem of centralized management of dispersed information and decentralized services of centralized information and effectively support all kinds of perception resources and processing in the form of data, so as to realize service-oriented on-demand aggregation and application.

The basic equipment layer is mainly composed of the intelligent perception layer and the medical and health private network, with different kinds of sensors and sensing networks, which are connected with the mobile terminal at one end and the cloud service system at the other end. The intelligent perception layer plays the role of a data bridge, which enables efficient access to comprehensive relevant medical information, including image recognition and data transmission. Through three kinds of access, namely, overall planning by operators, special line access, and Internet access via a virtual private network (VPN), the medical and health private network can not only realize information coordination in the medical field but also the integration, sharing, and security of the networks of other fields of the smart city, so as to realize the transmission and unified management of the whole smart city network.

The standard and regulation system is the basic work of the construction of WIT120 and the criterion for the application and development of all links. Under the principle of "Unified standard, unified code and unified interface", the construction of WIT120 follows the established standards and technical routes of business standards combined and standardized data definition. The standard and regulation system mainly includes eight regulation systems, namely, the health standard system of WIT120, data standard and information exchange standard for electronic health records and electronic medical records, management regulations of the relevant institutions of the WIT120 health system, management regulations of the resident electronic health records, standards for intervention of the information system of medical and health institutions, standards for information sharing of medical resources, standards for information sharing of health management, and management of the standard and regulation system. It plays different normative roles in different departments, so as to realize the integrated standardization of WIT120 and avoid unnecessary risks in the construction of WIT120.

The security guarantee system is mainly constructed from six aspects: physical security, network security, host security, application security, data security, and security management, which provide powerful technical support for the security protection of the construction of WIT120. Through the adoption of multi-level and multi-faceted technical means and methods, comprehensive protection, monitoring, response, and other security measures, it can ensure that the whole WIT120 system is equipped with safety protection, monitoring and management, testing and evaluation, emergency response, and other capabilities.

1.2.2.3 *Technical structure*

Technically, the structure of WIT120 includes the terminal layer, the network layer, the platform layer, and the application layer (Fig. 1.12). The terminal layer can serve as either the receiving end or the sending end. As the receiving end of information, it is mainly responsible for collecting information continuously, comprehensively, and rapidly, and as the sending end of information, it is responsible for displaying the information stored in the cloud system.

Artificial intelligence devices can integrate the doctors' workstation, the nurses' workstation, and imaging and examination work to provide patients with an unmanned guide for medical services. At the same time, the patients' vital signs are continuously monitored in real time. It can also transmit patients' vital sign data and emergency alarm information to medical staff via 5G. By obtaining comprehensive health information about the patients in a timely manner, the medical staff can make a prompt diagnosis and provide medical treatment for the patients, so as to improve the recovery rate of patients and reduce the fatality rate.

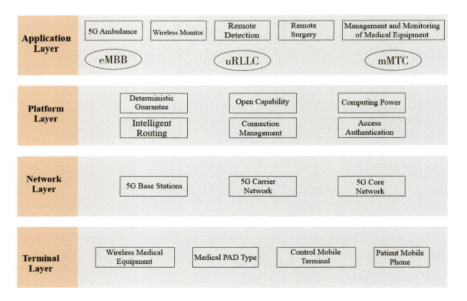

Figure 1.12   5G architecture diagram of the WIT120 technology.

The network layer is mainly responsible for real-time, reliable, and secure information transmission. The network layer covers a wide range of areas, from hospitals to community clinics, from large imaging devices to wearable devices, and from independent personality networks to shared networks. With the advent of 5G technology, the information among neighborhoods can be transmitted in a real-time manner with high speed and low delay through a wide connection.

With the ability of intelligent, accurate, and efficient information processing, the platform layer mainly stores, integrates, and analyzes the collected information and plays a transitional role in connecting the preceding and the following, in which artificial intelligence, cloud storage, and other information technologies are used to sort out and analyze the chaotic information collected from all sources. When useful information needs to be extracted, it can output valuable data at a high speed.

The application layer, as a concentrated embodiment of the value of 5G technology and medical integration, involves a wide range of levels, such as medical devices, telemedicine, and mobile personalized devices. The three features of the 5G network, namely, high speed, low delay, and wide connection, will facilitate the seamless connection of information between hospitals and patients, thus saving time and cost. These features are mainly reflected in the aspects of out-of-hospital first aid, in-hospital monitoring, intelligent medical operation, and telemedicine.

1.2.3 *Composition of WIT120*

1.2.3.1 *Smart hospital system*

The concept of "smart hospital", as a derivative concept of "smart earth", was first proposed by IBM. Smart hospital means to realize "one-stop" medical services through the "Internet of Things" and the Internet with the full use of the new generation of Internet technology in the medical and health industry and application of sensors to every link of the hospital, which improved efficiency of medical care within the hospital with more accurate and efficient diagnosis and treatment through supercomputers and cloud computing. Through various intelligent medical apparatus and instruments, intelligent medical platforms, as well as intelligent medical applications, "smart hospitals" organically connect patients, diagnosis and treatment process and the medical personnel, and high informationization, automation, mobility and intelligence in diagnosis, treatment, rehabilitation, payment, health management, and other links. So, the procedures for patients can be simplified while providing better quality care.

1.2.3.2 *Regional health system*

The core of the regional health system is the management of family health records and the provision of basic healthcare. It requires the community resources to be fully mobilized to give full play to the systematic functions of prevention, healthcare, diagnosis and treatment, rehabilitation, and health education within the community. According to the information structure standards of the hospital, the latest resident health records and electronic medical records shall also be provided in the community health information platform system.

The regional health system has three core contents, namely, resident health records, resident health management, and community medical services. These can be described as follows:

(1) *Resident health records*: The contents of resident health records include basic information, past medical history, family medical history, simple physical examination, health status, behavioral risk factors, sub-health status, and allergy history. Resident health records recording residents' every visit to a doctor in detail should be established and improved, so that doctors can quickly, completely, and accurately understand the patients' medical history and make accurate diagnoses.
(2) *Resident health management*: (i) *Planned immunization of children*: As an important part of the resident health records, the children's immunization plan should be recorded to ensure that no vaccines are omitted or repeated, and the state's requirements for the children's immunization should be followed. (ii) *Health education*: Community hospitals can use WeChat push, VR (virtual reality), and other new information means to inform about health science education effectively. (iii) *Disease prevention and rehabilitation*: Based on resident health records, Internet companies can conduct a predictive analysis through Big Data, provide health warnings and health advice with data exceeding standards, regularly provide health summary, and develop personalized "health guidelines", so as to maintain the supervision of patient data. (iv) *Chronic disease*

management: With the increasing aging of the society, the incidence of chronic diseases is also on the rise. Services like regular physical examination or smart wearable devices provided by community hospitals can be used to monitor the development of patients' conditions, and information can be synchronized to the equipment of doctors in charge, so that the doctors in charge can adjust treatment plans according to needs.
(3) *Community medical services*: (i) *Basic medical services and health management*: Community doctors can deal with minor diseases of some residents in the community by seeing patients in the clinics, visiting services, and even remote video services, so as to meet the general health needs of residents in the community. Community physicians can also regularly monitor and track patients' physical conditions and drug use through medical monitoring tools set up in patients' homes and sensors connected to these tools. The analysis results will be sent to the patient's family members and medical staff in a timely manner, so that the patient's family members can have detailed knowledge about the patient's condition and the medical staff can formulate the targeted medical plan in time. (ii) *Achieving hierarchical diagnosis and treatment and seamlessly docking with large hospitals*: After establishing the medical information integration platform, community hospitals will integrate the medical information of patients and realize the interconnection between the platform and large hospitals. When community doctors judge that the current medical conditions cannot meet the treatment needs of patients, patients can be transferred to large hospitals in a timely manner to ensure timely and effective treatment.

1.2.3.3 *Family health system*

The common problems that exist in family health of our country are as follows: (1) The weak awareness of the importance of regular physical examination can be noted. It is often the obvious symptoms that lead to hospital treatment, thus missing the best time for treatment; (2) Some patients do not have enough understanding of chronic diseases. Hence, they may not keep up with the regular intake of medication and regular review, believing that they're cured when symptoms disappear, which leads to the delayed treatment of the disease.

24 *The World of 5G: Intelligent Medicine*

The family health system is designed for "early prevention and long-term follow-up". The system, based on smart wearable devices and 5G technology, monitors users' life signs in real time. When users use the general medical devices, such as blood glucose meter, electronic sphygmomanometer, and electronic thermometer, the built-in wireless data acquisition module of the device will automatically transmit the data from the medical device to the intelligent mobile device wirelessly. Then, the data will be uniformly transmitted to the monitoring management platform of the corresponding hospital of the user, and the data will be analyzed by professional medical personnel, and corresponding treatment suggestions and plans will be put forward according to the user's condition. At the same time, the treatment suggestion and plan would be fed back to the individual through the information interactive server, so that the user can know his/her condition and conduct treatment according to the treatment suggestion and plan. When the user sees a doctor in the corresponding hospital or community, the doctor can check the user's daily health data through data collection and server query, which is helpful for diagnosis.

1.2.4 *Application of WIT120*

The cooperation between the traditional medical industry and Internet companies has greatly improved the efficiency of medical staff through the application of cutting-edge technologies and information products launched for hospitals to solve modern medical problems. Typical applications include smart outpatient service, smart ward, smart health management, and mobile medical library.

1.2.4.1 *Smart outpatient service*

The smart outpatient service can simplify the medical services and provide a better medical experience for patients through the use of intelligent products and information technology in the hospital outpatient service. The smart outpatient service includes the following aspects:

(1) *Intelligent hospital guidance system*: The traditional hospital guide is conducted by the front desk nurses, who are always fully occupied in most of the hospitals in our country. Through intelligent guidance,

patients will be guided to the corresponding department for treatment depending on the judgment made by artificial intelligence based on the symptoms and relevant information of the patients collected through the intelligent guidance machine in the outpatient hall or the mobile phone app. Intelligent guidance can not only reduce the workload of nurses but also deal with some problems and simple services frequently consulted by patients, thus improving the overall satisfaction of patients.

(2) *Intelligent registration system*: Traditional registration can only be made at the outpatient counter and cannot be made in advance. Intelligent registration provides patients with easy access to the introduction of departments and experts, doctor's schedule, doctor's current residual appointments, and other information through the outpatient terminal or mobile phone app, through which patients can make appointments with a designated doctor during his "free" time before going to the hospital at the time of appointment, saving the time of queuing for registration.

(3) *Intelligent queuing and calling system*: The traditional way of making an appointment with a doctor is usually done by swiping a card or checking in at the triage desk. While the smart outpatient system can offer online queuing and calling, by which patients can queue and call online through the relevant WeChat public account or the hospital app, with updated information about the number of people queuing in front of them, so as to arrange their own time.

(4) *Smart payment system*: The traditional way of outpatient payment is usually done at the counter, and the payment window is often set in the outpatient hall. Patients need to go back and forth to the department and hall repeatedly for multiple examinations, which is very inconvenient. In addition, offline medical insurance settlement also has disadvantages such as complicated settlement procedures and long time. The smart outpatient service provides the function of online payment to allow patients to pay medical bills online (including medical insurance settlement), optimize the medical treatment process, and improve patients' medical treatment experience.

(5) *Smart pharmacy*: At a traditional pharmacy, to get their medicine, patients hand a paper receipt to the pharmacist, who will then fish various drugs from the shelves by memory or simple labels, check the patient's information and dose after finding, before putting the drugs

Figure 1.13   Smart pharmacy.

into the bag to give to the patients. This method obviously has a few problems such as low efficiency of drug-taking and error-prone manual checking. The smart pharmacy, which can directly confirm the patients' prescriptions through the network without paper certificates and realize the full automation of drug collection and delivery through mechanical devices, reduce the intermediate links in a safe and reliable manner and effectively reduce the patients' waiting time (Fig. 1.13).

1.2.4.2 *Smart ward*

The smart ward, as an application integrated information service system of "hospital–nurse station–ward", will collect and sort the scattered medical data and display them through the intelligent terminal, presenting timely and accurate information for medical staff and patients. The smart ward can reduce medical nursing errors, optimize the nursing process, improve the working efficiency of the medical staff, improve the patients' medical experience, and improve medical service quality through the interventions at multiple links. The smart ward includes the following aspects:

(1) *Smart bedside interactive system*: The smart bedside interactive system is a "one-stop" medical information platform equipped beside the bed. As a replacement for the traditional handwritten bedside card, the smart bedside interactive system realized the whole paperless process, and the data-based storage can effectively avoid the medical problems caused by the loss of data. To provide a quality and convenient in-hospital environment for hospitalized patients, the system also serves as an intelligent service platform, which can provide patients with in-hospital information inquiry and self-service business services as well as entertainment.
(2) *Intelligent monitor in nurse station*: Intelligent monitor in nurse station is a centralized and visualized information processing platform. With the assistance of other measuring devices in the ward, the status of all patients in the ward can be monitored at the same time and synchronized in real time, enabling medical staff to "keep their eyes and ears open" while sitting in the office, which is conducive to improving the management efficiency of nurses. In addition, the platform also has the functions of reminder of patient call, infusion monitoring, nurse handover, etc., which can further optimize the hospital management process and make nursing work more reasonable.
(3) *Electronic doorplate*: Electronic doorplate is a kind of multimedia platform for the management of ward bed resources. Through the connection with the database of the nurse station, the electronic doorplate can realize the centralized visualization of the ward information. It can display the ward number, bed number, patient information, the information of the ward attending doctor, and responsible nurse. Moreover, it can read the information of all departments and update the patient information synchronously in real time, so as to effectively avoid the problem of untimely update and provide information navigation for the patient's family members and medical staff.
(4) *Mobile nursing system*: The mobile nursing system serves as the right-hand man in the process of hospital treatment and nursing as well as the supervisor of the medical staff. The system is mainly used for intelligent tracking of the whole process of the actual execution of medical advice, including admission management, nursing management, sign collection, medical advice verification, query of inspection

results, and real-time nursing monitoring. This is helpful to standardize nursing behavior, optimize the nursing process, as well as improve nursing efficiency and patient satisfaction.

1.2.4.3 Smart health management system

The smart health management system is composed of smart health risk assessment device/smart wearable device, Big Data platform for smart health management, computer background, or mobile phone app. Data collected in real time through the smart devices worn by the users will be uploaded to the hospital information system through the private network for analysis before feeding back to the terminals of the users, who can adjust their life or medication according to the "guidance" of the system, so as to realize the intelligent health management of the users (Fig. 1.14). The smart health management system includes the following aspects:

(1) *Disease prevention through daily collection of life data*: In fact, most of the diseases come from our unhealthy habits, such as sitting too long, addiction to alcohol or high-fat diets. Smart wearable devices can help users monitor small details in their lives, then upload data information to servers for analysis, so as to predict current health risks, and provide "guidance" to reduce the risk of illness.
(2) *Management of chronic diseases*: Due to the special nature of chronic diseases, patients with chronic diseases often need to take long-term medication and check regularly. The smart health management system, equipped with blood glucose meters, electronic blood pressure meters, electronic thermometers, and other medical instruments, will automatically transmit data to the monitoring and management platform of the corresponding hospital. Then, the professional doctors will carry out diagnosis and provide feedback on the treatment as well as advice, so that easy stay-at-home self-examination can be achieved, and the development of the disease can be firmly controlled.
(3) *Clinical research analysis*: The method utilized for randomized controlled trials is commonly used in clinical research, either for discussing the pros and cons of surgery or for some retrospective studies. The data the patient saves and uploads to the cloud regularly out of habit can be directly retrieved from the cloud by the researchers for analysis. This will greatly reduce the workload of clinical research and shorten the period of clinical research.

Intelligent Medicine 29

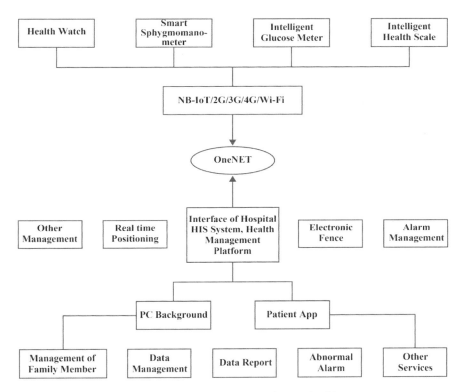

Figure 1.14   Mode diagram of smart health.

1.2.4.4 *Mobile medical library*

Despite the popularity of e-books nowadays, medical literature in special fields, being different from novels and magazines which can be bought in bookstores or searched on the Internet at will, can only be accessed after registering on relevant websites and paying for it in many cases. This undoubtedly increases the difficulty in the spread of medical knowledge. With the continuous development of intelligent mobile terminals and the expansion of social demand, software developers began to excavate and sort out medical resources to expand their business scope. For example, medicines, diseases, and symptoms from authoritative medical dictionaries, clinical case analysis, and even online reading and downloading of medical journals can be easily accessed via the mobile phone, which has brought great convenience to medical workers.

At the same time, medical knowledge service is not only targeted at medical workers but also the public who are thirsty for medical knowledge featuring "popularity" and "authoritativeness". Attention should be paid to the "authenticity" of medical information released on the Internet, for which various knowledge platforms, together with hospital experts, have successively launched medical science videos for patients to present quality and authoritative health knowledge to patients to help them establish correct health concepts.

5G technology, like 2G, 3G, and 4G mobile network technology, belongs to the digital cellular network, but with the rate its user experienced 10 times that of 4G mobile network technology, up to 10 Gb/s, and with a delay of less than 1 ms, 5G network undoubtedly provides a new solution for remote refined medical conduct. In October 2019, the Ministry of Industry and Information Technology issued China's first 5G radio communication equipment access license, with the approval of network access of 5G base station. 5G networks are embarking on the way to diversified, intelligent, and integrated development. At the end of October 2019, China's three major mobile telecom operators announced commercial 5G packages. With the formal commercial use of 5G and its integration with cutting-edge technologies such as Big Data, Internet+, artificial intelligence, and blockchain, WIT120 in the 5G era has shown great influence and vitality in intelligent diagnosis, data analysis, system optimization, and other aspects. The emergence of 5G technology is expected to push the human medical level into a new era.

Chapter 2

Making Distant Diagnosis and Treatment Possible with 5G

The year 2019 is called "the first year of the commercial use of 5G network in China" by industry insiders. The emergence and application of 5G could not have come at a better time against the backdrop of China's aging population and rising public health demand. 5G network, with features such as high speed, low delay, and wide connection meets exactly the needs of future medicine. 5G can provide strong support for the telemedicine service process with its advantages such as user experience rate that is 10 times higher than the 4G network, connection density 100 times, and transmission delay less than 1 ms. The difficulty in seeking medical services and the uneven distribution of medical resources have always been the pain points and difficulties for patients as well as for the development of the medical industry. 5G applications in the medical industry will serve for a harmonious doctor–patient relationship upon tremendous changes in the medical service model to better satisfy the patients in the process of medical services in the fields of hospital guidance of outpatients, remote medical treatment, medical imaging, automotive first aid, and medical digital services through the integration between the Internet and the medical industry. High-tech technologies such as artificial intelligence, Big Data, Internet of Things, and cloud computing brought about by the vigorous development of 5G technology have provided strong support for the construction of an intelligent information service system that fully covers people's livelihood, health, and medical care and realized the combination of online and offline Internet medical services.

2.1 Seeing Doctors with 5G Network at Your Side

2.1.1 *5G outpatient service — National experts at your side*

2.1.1.1 *Diagnosis and treatment without leaving home*

Driven by 5G technology, the development of WIT120 might double. Nowadays, patients can refer to the major integrated platforms of medical information for easy access to the expert resources of the medical industry all over the country instead of going to the hospitals for the data of relevant experts as before.

Over the platforms, patients can look through the complete resumes, major directions, and areas of expertise of local and national well-known experts. They can not only find an expert doctor suitable for their conditions according to their actual situations but also input relevant symptoms and follow the guidance of the intelligent customer service of the platform to get medical services. They can also find the schedule and registration information of the relevant doctors to avoid waiting in line at the hospital before seeing a doctor. With the popularization of 5G technology, not only can we go to the hospitals for medical service, but we can also go see AI (artificial intelligence) doctors, who will be online 24/7, like "iDoctor" developed by Zhuhai Health Cloud. Users can easily interact with "iDoctor" through voice or text input. Driven by Big Data, "iDoctor" is able to answer simple health questions, popularize health knowledge, and provide suggestions for patients about medical treatment, which greatly releases medical human resources and improves service efficiency.

2.1.1.2 *The intelligent hospital guidance robots put into use*

In May 2019, the on-site experience of guidance robots, VR newborn visiting, and remote video conference were officially offered during a press conference of 5G Smart Hospital held in the outpatient hall of Jinjiang Branch of the West China Second Hospital of Sichuan University. The 5G intelligent guidance robots placed in the hall of the outpatient department can provide services like interactive navigation and guidance, AI medical question and answer, in-hospital expert introduction to patients in the 5G network environment, improving patients' medical treatment experience, and the efficiency of medical staff (from the Chinadaily.com.cn). Unlike traditional robots, these robots have functions such as semantic recognition and picture recognition, which can be of great help in providing medical guidance services for patients, especially elderly patients who have language or mobility difficulties or do not understand the medical procedures. Through the TV system, these robots build a smart hospital information network platform integrating the functions of information system release, publicity and education through TV and film, health science popularization, remote medical services, and live operation through the interaction between patients and medical staff, medical institutions and medical equipment, which not only establish distance education and medical training system for hospitals through the integration of medical resources but also greatly improve the level of medical services for patients' enhanced sense of experience and satisfaction with hospitals (Fig. 2.1).

2.1.1.3 *The efficiency of medical treatment greatly improved*

According to a third-party satisfaction survey on medical institutions, the long queue time is one of the main factors for the dissatisfaction of

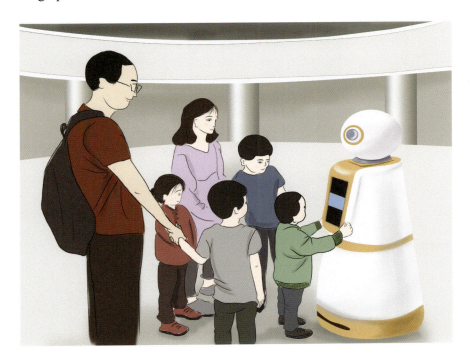

Figure 2.1   Citizens are interacting with a 5G intelligent guidance robot.

patients over the years. Roughly divided into the steps of "registration–reporting to the triage desk–waiting for calling–getting medical services–payment–examination–getting medicine", the traditional process to get hospital medical services wastes most of the patients' time while waiting in line, which seriously affects their medical experience. The promotion of 5G technology makes the information connection between patients and hospitals closer. Through face recognition technology, patients can quickly complete the steps of registration and payment, so as to avoid the tedious queuing. With 5G high-speed transmission, the medical staff can grasp the data of vital signs and image examination, health records, and other relevant information of the patients before diagnosis and treatment, which greatly reduce the time for medical treatment, thus thoroughly transforming and optimizing the service process of traditional hospitals and improving the efficiency of medical treatment.

2.1.1.4 *The chances of infection greatly reduced*

Novel Coronavirus, as the hottest topic of the society in 2020, is even more contagious and has greatly influenced the work and life of people in China and even the world, compared to SARS in 2003. Through the pandemic, not only have we seen the determination of medical workers to work together as one to fight against the pandemic but also the self-discipline and cooperation of citizens and villagers from all over the country in preventing and controlling the pandemic. However, how patients suffering from other diseases can seek medical treatment during the pandemic has become a big problem. As a crowded place, the hospital itself is an area with difficulties and challenges in the prevention and control of infectious diseases. Then, how to control the spread of the pandemic while ensuring the timely diagnosis and treatment of patients? 5G online outpatient service can solve this problem well. Through 5G online outpatient service, patients can get a timely diagnosis from doctors at home, which not only eliminates the tedious step of registration but also avoids contact with the crowd, greatly reducing the risk of infection.

2.1.2 *5G brainstorming — Seeing a doctor who is a thousand miles away*

The difficulty of getting medical services has always been a hot topic because of people's livelihood. According to relevant surveys, about half of the residents in China will not seek medical treatment until there are symptoms of illness, and about 29% of the residents who should be hospitalized choose not to. Over time, minor illnesses turn into major ones, and mild illnesses become serious ones. This is especially true for some patients with chronic diseases. This situation is particularly serious in some remote areas in China. Even with the medical treatment cost at their own expense greatly reduced by the more perfect medical insurance policy now, most patients with minor or even serious illnesses still choose not to get treated due to the limited medical recourses in villages and towns and the distance from the big cities, thus missing the best time to treat the diseases. Sometimes, patients, because of the delay due to the long distance, die before even reaching the hospital. Now with 5G technology, things will go toward a bright future.

2.1.2.1 *What does 5G medical bring us?*

In March 2019, the General Hospital of the People's Liberation Army completed the country's first remote human surgery utilizing the 5G network (http://www.xinhuanet.com). In May 2019, several experts from the Cancer Prevention and Treatment Center of Sun Yat-sen University conducted "one-to-many" remote guidance in minimally invasive surgeries in Zhuhai People's Hospital, Shenzhen Hospital of Peking University, and Gaozhou People's Hospital by using 5G technology (http://www.sciencenet.cn/).

Telemedicine based on 4G technology has been launched by some hospitals previously, but the delayed transmission and the poor quality of video images made it difficult for doctors to communicate with patients, which eventually lead to the deterioration of the quality of medical services. This is clear evidence that it is still difficult for telemedicine to be widely popularized, not to mention for an operation to be as precise as remote surgery, in which any delay between the surgeon and the device can be fatal to the patient.

The birth of 5G technology, with the overall improvement in the network that to a large extent meets the needs of real time, high efficiency, and stability in medical treatment, has greatly improved this situation. Based on real-time images, video calls, and voice calls, 5G technology can realize remote diagnosis, remote treatment, and even remote surgery more effectively. With the support of 5G technology, the fidelity of the images for remote diagnosis and treatment is guaranteed, and even if

36 *The World of 5G: Intelligent Medicine*

magnified by 20 times, the patient's wound or words on the medical record will still be clearly recognized. Doctors can understand the conditions of patients' overall condition and medical records through high-definition cameras and interact with patients in real time, ensuring the accuracy of remote diagnosis.

Take image data as an example, previously county hospitals were unable to build 3D (three-dimensional) models, while CT (computed tomography) images with the size of more than 10 gigabytes could only be copied into hard disks or transmitted over the Internet, requiring hours of downloading. With the support of 5G, these Big Data of medical images can be quickly transmitted, filed and browsed, and downloaded in just a few minutes. Through these 3D models, the medical staff can have a clear and direct view of the preoperative situation of the patient's surgical site and improve the success rate of surgery (Fig. 2.2).

5G network connections established between large grade-A class-three hospitals and primary medical institutions make it possible that patients in remote areas can enjoy services from well-known experts in local hospitals, with the economic burden of patients alleviated for a large amount of treatment expenses is saved. Someone has made a calculation, when patients in remote areas go to big hospitals in other regions, not only

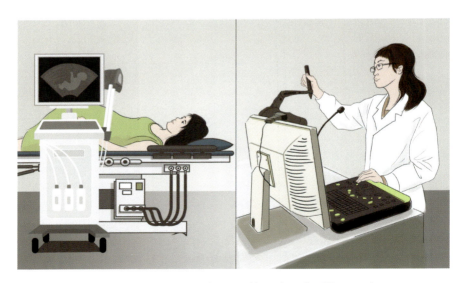

Figure 2.2   Remote B-ultrasound based on the 5G network.

will the cost of surgery and other treatments differ from that of local hospitals, but they will also have to pay for travel and accommodation of their accompanying families, and because the prices of medical consumables are different in the two places and the reimbursement standard of medical insurance is also different, so the actual difference of treatment cost of the two places may be huge. Telemedicine enables patients to enjoy expert-level diagnosis and treatment at home without paying excessive costs and get their "serious illnesses treated without leaving the county".

2.1.2.2 *The world's first 5G remote full outpatient service started*

In September 2019, the world's first 5G remote full outpatient service was launched between Hainan Hospital of the PLA General Hospital and Sansha People's Hospital of Hainan Province. The service not only enables citizens on the Island of Sansha to enjoy high-quality medical services without having to travel long distances but also lays a foundation to improve the primary medical care (http://www.people.cn).

The highlight and innovation of this 5G remote full outpatient service featured "whole", that is, the whole process, whole time, and the whole field of outpatient diagnosis through the remote system. The whole process means that outpatient registration, consultation and physical examination, examination data, preliminary diagnosis, and prescription of drugs can all be completed online through the remote system. Whole time means that in the process of diagnosis and treatment, real-time video, audio, and image data can be transmitted between the two hospitals to assist the real-time control of inspection instruments and equipment, and real-time diagnosis and treatment services can be provided to patients. The whole field means that the telemedicine service is not limited to a single department but the cooperation among the clinical clinic, auxiliary departments, outpatient pharmacy, and other departments.

2.1.2.3 *5G remote surgery*

As one of the most advanced fields of medicine, surgical operation not only requires surgeons of very high medical knowledge and skills but also the accuracy of surgical equipment. For remote surgery, the speed of transmission between the two devices is particularly important.

In May 2019, Director Wan, director of the General Surgery Department of the Second Affiliated Hospital of Anhui Medical University, performed a remote cholecystectomy.

The operation began at 9 o'clock, when the end of the laparoscope was extended to the surgical site of the patient after the completion of the preoperative work. "The surgical visual field is not complete, please wake the surgical robot and adjust the angle of the robotic arm". With voice control, Director Wan remotely operated the surgical robot to adjust the visual field to the optimal angle. The images of the patient's abdomen being cut open and the gallbladder polyp were clearly projected on the big screen in front of Wan with a delay of less than 0.1 s. Director Wan performed the operation on the patient who was 256 km away by operating the robot arm remotely, during which there was no signal jam or operation delay despite the long distance. After the successful completion of the operation, Director Wan summed up the remote operation in one word, immersive (www.hinews.cn).

With the development and improvement of 5G technology, more and more remote surgeries will be performed, which will greatly improve the efficiency of medical services. In November 2019, 5G remote surgery was selected as one of the Top Ten Events of the Future Science and Technology in China, which also reflects its landmark role in the aspect of the mode of medical service.

2.1.2.4 More efforts still needed for the development of 5G medical services

Although 5G medical has begun to benefit people with its advantages, there are still many restrictions on its promotion. First, the costs are too high. The millimeter wave used by 5G has disadvantages such as poor penetration, large signal attenuation, small coverage, and being blocked easily. Therefore, to achieve full coverage of 5G signal in large hospitals, thousands of indoor base stations are often required, costing more than RMB 1 billion yuan, not including outdoor signal base stations. In remote areas with poor communication infrastructure, the cost can be even higher, and the "sky-high construction fee" is the primary obstacle to the development and promotion of 5G medical services.

Secondly, many legal issues will arise concerning 5G medical treatment. For example, there is still no definite mechanism of responsibility division for any possible accident in remote surgery, as the National Health Commission has reminded us that there are certain risks in remote surgery. The ombudsman of the Medical Administration and Hospital Authority of National Health Commission said that scientific and prudent exploration should be followed based on the current network technology and laws of medical science.

In addition, there is still no mature standard system for 5G medical and health because there is no unified standard for access mode and data format of terminal equipment, and there are still no proper solutions to the security risks of huge data. Thus, the development of 5G medical service still has a long way to go.

2.1.3 *5G quick wits — Strategize wisely*

When it comes to 5G medical, 5G remote surgery is usually the first thing that comes to our minds. In fact, 5G is showing more and more strong vitality and influence in the field of health and medical services, such as in medical treatment, scientific research, teaching, and other aspects and plays a crucial role in accelerating the construction of "healthy China" and promoting the development of the medical and health industry. So, what important roles do 5G play in the daily operation of hospitals?

2.1.3.1 *5G mobile medical care*

Due to the lack of medical staff, traditional medical services can't offer timely ward rounds in departments with many patients. Mobile medical services, with the newly launched ward rounds robot, as well as the 5G network, greatly improved the efficiency of doctors through remote and real-time ward rounds with extended diagnosis and treatment services at the bedside of patients. This, combined with the 5G network, can allow doctors to simply operate a joystick or smartphone to move the robot, which is remotely controlled over a 5G network, to the patient's bedside, where a real-time video conversation can be conducted with the robot's head camera to get to know the change in the patients' condition. Meanwhile, multiple sensors equipped in the ward round robot can collect biochemical and pathological data of the patients in real time to assist the doctors in diagnosis. In addition, in the wards of radiology department and infectious diseases department that have a high risk of infection,

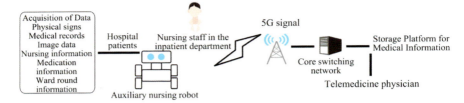

Figure 2.3   5G schematic diagram of mobile medical care.

concerning the safety of medical staff, the medical assistant robot can be used to offer bedside nursing services for the patients through the 5G network remote control (Fig. 2.3).

2.1.3.2 *5G telemedicine training*

Medical education is the education and training provided for medical and health technicians, including doctors, nurses, and medical technicians, mainly in the form of conferences and lectures, case discussions, and training sessions on the technical operation. It is particularly important to strengthen the grassroots doctors in consultation and operation through medical education, due to the uneven distribution of the medical resources in China as well as the different backgrounds of medical personnel and the large gap between the doctors in large grade-A class-three hospitals and the grassroots doctors can make up for these shortcomings.

Before the emergence of 5G telemedicine training, medical education in primary hospitals was usually conducted through surgical videos, lectures by experts, or further training in medical education in major hospitals for grassroots doctors. Though to some extent video learning can be effective, due to the lack of real-time communication, earners often fail to grasp some operational details well, so the effect of training is considerably compromised. Lectures by experts or further study in big hospitals will cost a lot of time in traveling and it is a waste of human resources.

5G telemedicine training will connect the endoscopes in operating rooms or cameras with multimedia broadcast equipment and transmit the converted audio and video signals to the consultation center through 5G base stations. Relevant medical staff who are not in the operating room can learn and observe synchronously on 5G mobile phones, 5G terminals,

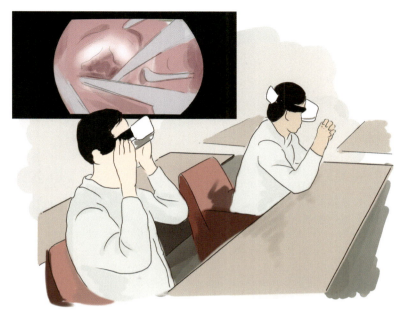

Figure 2.4   Grassroots doctors learn surgical operation remotely through VR equipment.

and VR devices or even communicate with the teaching staff in real time through the remote medical teaching platforms.

Through 5G telemedicine training, learners or grassroots doctors will have more learning channels to observe the difficult surgeries when performed by experts and better master the professional skills, which is of great help to share high-quality medical resources, improve the medical level of grassroots doctors, and balance the unequal distribution of medical resources (Fig. 2.4).

2.1.4 *5G cloud medical records — Easy access to medical information*

With the deepening of hospital informatization and the continuous development of the application of information technology in the medical industry, medical data storage and security sharing have become a trend. EMR (Electronic Medical Record) has been widely used in the medical industry. After years of accumulation, EMR has collected a massive amount of medical records and gradually entered the era of cloud data. The large amount of effective information in these cloud medical records has become a huge source of wealth for doctors and patients. The cloud medical record, which is totally different from traditional paper medical records, is the data information that will improve patients' satisfaction with medical services and improve medical services in the medical industry. Cloud medical records can not only enable data sharing and mutual recognition but also strengthen the cross-regional collaborative management and application of high-quality resources. The cloud medical record is not just a simple medical record but also a set of medical network disks independent of the clinical business system and independent in the collection of data of in-hospital and out-hospital disease courses.

Cloud medical records can help realize the sharing of medical resources upon the advantage of the network and the full utilization of the medical information technology of hospitals (Fig. 2.5). Through the telemedicine system, the upper medical institutions and medical managers can understand the utilization of hospital health resources and the health status of patients in real time. Primary-level medical institutions can keep track of the treatment of patients in the hospital in real time and realize the cooperation of out-of-hospital medical services and strengthen the inpatient management of patients. The hospital can scientifically plan its information resources, optimize its business workflow, constantly innovate its medical service and management mode, maximize the integration of

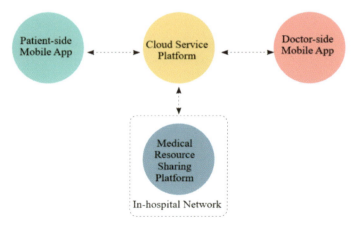

Figure 2.5 Architecture of cloud cases.

hospital information systems and the development and utilization of information resources, and greatly improve its own capacity of information construction and level of logistics support.

2.1.4.1 *The impact of cloud medical records on individuals*

The disadvantage of traditional paper medical records is that they're inconvenient to carry, difficult to keep, and easy to lose. The accidental loss of the medical record out of the carelessness of the patient will not only lead to the failure that the doctor cannot fully understand the patient's medical history in the following medical consultation, which is not only conducive to the doctor making further treatment plans but can also lead to the risk of the disclosure of patient's private information. Different from traditional paper-based medical records, with the medical institutions working as the main body, cloud medical records share the medical record information to individual patients, with personal health records supplemented by individuals and information on visits to hospitals in other places uploaded into the system. When patients come to the hospital for medical treatment, their previous medical information including examination reports, medical registration records, prescription records, medical fees, discharge summaries, etc., will be pushed to the cloud medical record app on their personal end devices after they download the cloud medical record app (Fig. 2.6) and bind their personal information. Such a cloud-sharing platform of medical records will not only completely record the health information of patients but also enable the patients with a comprehensive understanding of their own diagnosis and treatment.

It has the following advantages: (1) When patients visit hospitals, it can provide doctors with diagnosis and treatment records for reference so that the doctors can clearly and completely check up the patient's previous medical records. (2) It's easy to check medical records. Patients can view each prescription generated in each visit, as well as examination and pathological reports and other contents according to their will, in the system which supports classified viewing, such as viewing the previous reports of blood routine examination only. (3) *Instructions for drug use*: Patients can check up prescription-related drug information, including drug use, medication time, matters needing attention, and storage conditions. (4) *Health records*: With the smart blood pressure meter, the system can automatically record the patient's each measurement and conduct intelligent analysis. In addition to pushing various diagnosis and treatment

44   *The World of 5G: Intelligent Medicine*

Figure 2.6   Cloud medical records.

information, the system can improve patients' experience of receiving medical services and have a better understanding of their own diseases. At a time when doctor–patient relations are sensitive, sharing such data will not only simplify the process of patients' copying medical records and filing in various hospitals but also bridge the gap between doctors and patients.

2.1.4.2 *The use of cloud medical records in the healthcare industry*

The cloud medical records not only enable hospitals' interactions with the patients but also promotes the development of Internet diagnosis and treatment. The Peking University Cancer Hospital launched the app service of cloud medical records in recent years, which provides patients with digital medical records and various medical services, so as to realize the effective management of patients' health throughout their whole life cycle. It enables not only the storage of medical data internally in the hospital but also makes the data available to be checked up and saved by the patients themselves. At the same time, the cloud medical record app can also push various diagnosis and treatment information, which greatly improves patients' medical treatment experience. In addition, patients and medical staff can obtain medical data through the cloud medical record app and customize rich application services according to different application scenarios.

At the end of 2017, the Peking University Cancer Hospital began to jointly develop cloud medical records with manufacturers with mature technology in digital medical records. So, how can the risks of cloud medical records be managed? It is undeniable that in the era of Big Data, providing patients with digital medical records through the Internet will face great risks to the disclosure of patients' private data, so it is necessary to make great efforts in information security management. In the whole project of cloud medical records, the most critical and important work is to protect patient privacy and data security.

In terms of protecting patients' privacy, the cloud medical record system established by the Peking University Cancer Hospital adopts two methods, namely, SMS verification through the bound phone number and authentication to determine whether users have the right to access the information and effective action to protect the patients' private information and medical record data from various aspects and multiple perspectives. Hospitals require that the display of digital medical records on the cloud medical record app should be consistent with that of the paper medical records. However, in reality, medical record data involves many systems designed by different application developers, which lead to great differences among different systems in that some systems can export data in the form of images or PDF files directly, while others can only export structured data.

For this reason, the Peking University Cancer Hospital solved this problem through a set of automatic template tools specially designed to enable the system to generate structured data with a unified format. For example, it can generate questions about the patient's ID card and social security card information and even the patient's recent department to confirm the identity of the patient. In terms of data security, all data servers are set up within the hospital to fully ensure the controllability of data, and through data encryption, access control, system firewall, and other security measures, the security of data is guaranteed to the maximum content. In addition, in order to cope with unexpected server failures, the Peking

University Cancer Hospital has established a complete emergency plan for operation and maintenance, including pre-examination, monitoring and backup, as well as specifications for in-process fault handling, post-examination, and analysis. The operation and growing utilization of the app show the wide application and scientific feasibility of cloud medical records. With the consent of patients, medical staff can also collect basic data through cloud medical records for scientific research work.

2.2 Customized New Health Manager for You

In today's society, with the rapid development of science and technology, and the widespread availability of new technology, products and services in the consumer market are gradually diversified. The diversified products and services offered diversified choices for consumers, whose choices in turn determine the direction of market development. At the same time, with the rapid development of the national economy and the improved income, the consumption concept of the people has been gradually personalized and differentiated, which represents the new pursuits of various industries. Future healthcare will be more personalized, precise, and preventative, according to the survey. At the same time, future healthcare will not only focus on treatment but also on the management of personal health risks and prevention of diseases through lifestyle changes and customized lifestyles.

2.2.1 *Personalized medical care*

In healthcare services, patients and their families are eager to receive timely, targeted services from professionals that are better able to help them get out of pain or uneasiness. However, as is well known, each individual has different health status risks and different factors for disease. Even two people suffering from the same disease may vary concerning the conditions of their illness. Besides, people differ from each other in their health conditions, which are constantly changing, so the treatment suitable for some people may not be fit for others, for which healthcare programs should and must be personalized. However, few people around the country or even the world have the access to a private physician around the clock, and the current passive medical model continues to dominate the healthcare market. The serious marathon-like medical problems of uneven distribution of medical resources, the long journey to seek medical treatment in other cities, the long queue for medical services in hospitals, and the unguided rehabilitation outside hospitals have brought extremely poor experience to users of medical services. Therefore, an entirely new healthcare model needs to be developed to break down the current barriers to access to healthcare (Fig. 2.7).

The 21st century is the era of rapid development of information technology, when the development and construction of all industries are gradually informationized. Driven by information technology, China took the lead in putting forward the concept of Internet+ in 2015, leading the innovative combination of Internet technology and traditional industries in China. Facing the deficiencies of traditional industries, researchers, innovators, and creators from all industries have given full play to the potential of information and technology by combining the needs of the public with the innovative application of current technologies. Through the integration of network communication technology and traditional industries, the development of all industries has been accelerated, in addition to the emergence of Internet+ medical care.

The medical care industry, which is responsible for the "capital of revolution", namely, the health of the people, has promoted the informationization of medical care through the research and development of Internet+ medical services, bringing about a subversive change in the field

Figure 2.7 Personalized healthcare.

of medical care. The digitalization of medical services enables users to have convenient experiences like online banking and retail interactions, just by flipping their fingertips over their smart devices. In 2019, a world-class communications network battle ended with Huawei Technologies Co., Ltd. coming into the public view with its 5G technology. As the latest generation of cellular mobile communication technology, 5G network has advantages such as high speed, low delay, and wide connection.

Therefore, the 5G communication technology, once emerged, has quickly become a hot topic in today's society. With the heated concern of 5G+, the research on the application of 5G+ has shown a blowout development in various industries, with the Internet+ rapidly replaced by 5G+ and Internet+ medical services gradually evolved into 5G+ WIT120, which represents a new direction for the development of medical care. With the cooperation of Internet operators and information equipment providers, the medical care industry is gradually exploring a better, more convenient, and faster mode for personalized medical care meeting the needs of users in the transformation process from traditional medical care of Internet+ medical services to 5G+ WIT120.

With the development of 5G communication technology and researchers' in-depth exploration of 5G+ WIT120, medical health monitoring devices, clinical wearable devices, and remote sensors with low energy consumption and low bit rate are gradually appearing in the world of users, where tens of thousands of medical care devices constitute a large-scale ecosystem of medical Internet of Things. Through the mass collection and analysis of health data, which are cooperating with the deep learning and concentration of health data of cloud intelligence platform, medical personnel can offer automated healthcare services to users more widely, making it possible to provide more convenient and considerate personal health services for everyone in the future, in which they can scan the whole bodies of users anytime and anywhere for data to be intelligently analyzed through cloud computing, Big Data, and AI. After analysis, conclusions and relevant health suggestions can be given to users to get early prevention and treatment against any health risks.

In addition, through personalized health services, users can communicate with telemedicine experts individually, which can protect their privacy and allow them to enjoy medical services anytime and anywhere. For patients with some special diseases, such as malignant infectious diseases or patients in some remote areas, on the one hand, wearable devices can track patients' physical conditions in real time and provide them with "personal care", so that patients, especially the elderly and children with low immunity, can be spared from suffering more; on the other hand, wearable devices can timely respond to emergency conditions and isolate patients, reduce the contact between patients and others, inhibit the transmission of bacteria and viruses by way of cutting off its transmission route, protect vulnerable groups, and improve the utilization of medical resources and efficiency of medical workers from all aspects.

Moreover, healthy people can also use wearable devices to monitor their diet and fitness status, and based on the complete health reports of the users, corresponding medical nutrition experts and exercise rehabilitation doctors can make up personalized health plans for a healthier life for the users.

With the support of 5G, wearable devices can capture vital signs of the users and quickly and accurately transmit them to the central control room, where professional medical personnel will screen the relevant indicators and give timely intervention and realize national health monitoring. This technology bridges the geographical gap, provides users with round-the-clock care services, saves users' time and energy through a fast and convenient green channel of more personalized medical care for users, and brings innovation to the medical care industry.

2.2.2 *Management of personal health records*

Personal health records record a person's most basic physical conditions from birth to death. It covers the whole process of the occurrence, development, treatment, and outcome of a person's disease, which features continuity, dynamic, and comprehensiveness. The records of personal health, on the one hand, can warn the people against the adverse factors endangering their health, improve their health behavior (change unreasonable eating habits and bad living habits), and take targeted intervention measures; on the other hand, in case of illness or emergency, it can provide the medical staff with core information immediately, so that they can better understand the health of patients and better diagnose and treat them. Therefore, a comprehensive and detailed personal health record plays an indispensable role in personal medical care. Relevant studies have shown that the level of self-management of diabetic patients is positively correlated with the effect of blood glucose control. The management of personal health records has a positive effect on the improvement of life of diabetic patients, and improving the management effect can reduce or

50 *The World of 5G: Intelligent Medicine*

Figure 2.8   Management of personal health records.

delay the occurrence and aggravation of diabetic complications. Thus, it is necessary to manage personal health records (Fig. 2.8).

However, the management of personal health records is not an easy thing, which is mainly reflected in the following aspects: (1) The establishment of personal health records requires management staff of health records to collect relevant data and file the collected data after sorting, counting and analyzing them, which is a huge amount of work. (2) The establishment of personal health records requires keeping track of a person's physical condition in real time and recording all his physical and mental health-related behaviors. This requires the Management Center of Health Records to be adequately funded and equipped with appropriate facilities. (3) Personal health records are full of information of real-time tracking of a person's lifestyle and location, in which a lot of personal privacy may be involved. So, the security and privacy of files is extremely important. (4) For the retrieval and use of personal health files, fast, simple and safe access should also be correspondingly established.

The vast majority of documents related to personal files have always been in paper form for the time being, until some files have shifted from the traditional paper version to the electronic version in their management recently. This is because the traditional paper files not only require a lot of manpower for the sorting of all kinds of information but also need a lot of time for the query and worry about the spatial storage of files. Besides, there are other problems like wear and tear in the process of using files, aging problems, and "three proofing's" (moisture proofing, fireproofing, and theft proofing) in the storage process. With the gradual penetration of information technology into human life, personal health records have gradually become informationized. Informationized files not only save time and labor but also can be stored conveniently and can be quickly found and viewed. It saves manpower and material resources and promotes the progress of medical and healthcare services. It is an inevitable trend for personal health records to be informationized and managed through the computer system, which is an inevitable way for doctors and patients to use personal health records quickly and conveniently.

Compared to the paper personal health records, the advantages of the digitized personal health records (Fig. 2.9) are mainly reflected in the following aspects:

(1) *Easy storage*: The paper health records can be put into the computer to be transmitted and stored in the cloud. This not only makes its management informationized and systematized, and effectively solves the problem of insufficient storage for paper files but also can permanently preserve the files and solve the problems of paper wear and aging in the process of using.
(2) *Fast transmission*: Stored in the digital form on a specific medium, and encoded and decoded in the network terminals, information of

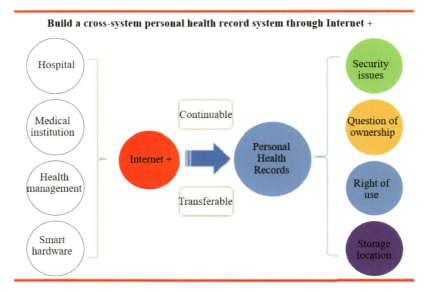

Figure 2.9 The system of personal health records.

digital records can be transmitted beyond the limits of time, space, and carrier. Users can read the information of stored records through any network terminal, effectively avoiding the problems that the paper file cannot be timely and efficiently obtained for there is only one copy in storage.

(3) *Various forms*: Electronic archives can record personal records in the forms of audio and video and reproduce the whole picture of recorded content more vividly, so as to make them diversified but not confined to the text records only.

(4) *Easy to use*: Informationized personal files will be stored uniformly in the cloud in the form of data codes after being input into the computer. The computer's permuterm index (a kind of index technology) can be used to quickly and accurately complete the retrieval of relevant information, and this information can be printed through output equipment for convenient use.

Of course, every coin has two sides, and the electronic personal health record has its drawbacks too. In addition to privacy concerns, digital personal health records are heavily affected by network coverage and transmission speed. When life and health are at risk, no one wants to see a reply of "loading, please wait". With the advent of the 5G era, this problem will be greatly improved. 5G has brought great convenience to our life, and the management of personal health records is no exception. For example, electronic personal health records contain a lot of information, such as texts, pictures, audio, and video, which all need informatization management, and the transmission process requires a lot of waiting time. This process can be completed in a very short time through 5G enabling, with advantages such as high speed, low delay, and wide connection, which further improves the efficiency of relevant personnel. In addition, when emergencies occur, the medical staff can quickly give targeted interventions, and 5G technology can also be used to uniformly customize apps for users, so that users' relevant information can be collected completely and their personal health records can be managed without deliberate attention.

The management of personal health records maximizes users' access to healthcare by providing targeted safeguards in the areas of disease intervention, healthcare guidance, and health risk assessment. Through further research on 5G technology, the comprehensive informatization of personal health records will not be far away thanks to 5G communication technology.

2.2.3 *Remote monitoring*

In the late 1950s, the two-way television system was first applied to the medical field in the United States. With the rapid development of electronic and communication technology, in the early 1960s, the US National Aeronautics and Space Administration (NASA) established a remote medical test bench, using microwave technology and satellite communications to provide remote monitoring service for astronauts. Medical experts on the ground could collect data on the physical conditions of astronauts through telemetry to know the physical health of astronauts in the weightless environment of space. Since then, relevant projects have been carried out in the United States and European countries, greatly promoting the development of remote monitoring (Fig. 2.10).

Using Internet technology, remote monitoring created a patient-centered remote consultation and continuous monitoring service system for patients in critical conditions, so as to avoid patients being admitted to hospitals and clinics. Remote monitoring generally includes three parts: remote

54 *The World of 5G: Intelligent Medicine*

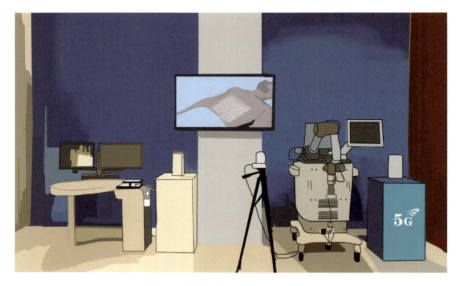

Figure 2.10   Remote monitoring.

monitoring center, remote monitoring equipment, and the communication network which connects them. The remote physiological information and medical signals are transmitted to the remote monitoring center through the communication network for analysis and diagnosis. 5G with the features of low delay and precise positioning can give continuous reports about the locations of patients through wearable monitoring devices, which will collect, process, and compute vital signs at the same time before transmitting the information to the remote monitoring center for medical staff to make timely diagnosis and treatment according to the physiological status of patients. In addition, remote monitoring of the elderly, patients with chronic diseases, as well as newborns and patients in ICUs (intensive care units) can provide the basis for timely health monitoring and medical intervention for these groups, greatly improving their health and life (Fig. 2.11).

2.2.3.1   *ECG telemonitor*

Cardiac rhythm monitoring is the main application of remote monitoring. The sudden onset and high risk of heart disease determine the high

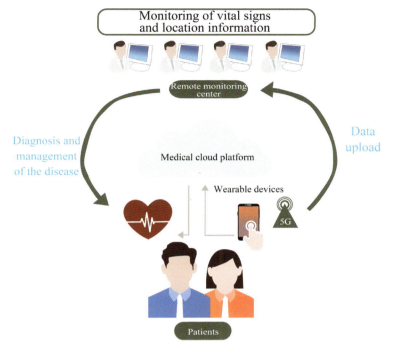

Figure 2.11 Architecture of the remote monitoring scheme.

requirements for the monitoring of patients with heart disease, leaving routine ECG examination and intensive care in hospitals far from meeting the monitoring needs of patients with heart disease.

In 1903, Dutch physiologist Einthoven transmitted an ECG signal to somewhere at a distance of 1,500 m for the first time through telephone lines. In 1960, physicians at an island clinic in the United States used telephone electrocardiogram technology to send an electrocardiogram of an island patient to the mainland through the phone line for diagnosis and consultation. Later, Daniel's heart medical company provided technical support to external ECG monitoring institutions such as telephone ECG remote monitoring centers and rehabilitation centers.

The commonly used ECG telemonitor system consists of patient-side ECG monitoring equipment, remote medical monitor center, and the communication connection between the two. At present, there are ECG monitoring products such as electrocardiogram short-time recorder and intelligent electrocardiogram monitoring equipment for patients on the market, among which the intelligent ECG monitoring equipment adopts long-time wireless real-time monitoring ECG and offers the functions of ECG recording for a long time and automatic transmission. When the detected abnormal ECG exceeds the alarm threshold, it can automatically transmit the ECG to the medical center for alarm in real time, which makes it suitable for patients with heart disease to use at home.

Since 2000, we have entered a new stage of remote ECG monitoring based on the wireless network, that is, the mobile remote ECG monitoring has been developed into network system remote ECG monitoring. By 2011, the rapid development of cloud computing and Big Data has extended simple ECG monitoring to the combined remote monitoring of blood pressure, blood oxygen, and respiration. Remote monitoring technology of network system is building a heart monitoring global village, where remote heart monitoring can be carried out at anytime and anywhere, as long as there is a network connection.

Patients and their families can monitor themselves at home by using mobile ECG and wristwatches with the function of ECG blood pressure monitoring and other monitoring equipment. Residential communities and community health service centers can also provide remote cardiac monitoring services, so that patients can get diagnosis and treatment from professional doctors and patients can also get timely rescue in case of emergency. With the advent of the 5G era, remote cardiac monitoring technologies such as the monitoring of ECG and blood pressure have entered the fast lane of Internet development in China. The upstream rate of 5G is about 14 times that of 4G, the downstream rate is about 15 times that of 4G, the comprehensive performance of the network is 100 times that of 4G, and the time delay reaches the level of milliseconds, which makes the whole remote monitoring operation process very smooth in the future.

2.2.3.2 Remote fetal monitoring

From the preparation of pregnancy to full-term pregnancy and delivery of a healthy and intellectually developed newborn, regular and timely fetal monitoring are necessary, through which the normal growth and development of the fetus in the whole gestation period can be protected, and the negative factors affecting the fetus can be eliminated in time, so as to reduce the occurrence of adverse characters in the human population.

Due to the need for multiple examinations, pregnant women often have to travel to and from the hospitals, which adds to the burden on pregnant women and their families.

As the most direct and intimate contact with the fetuses as well as the most effective guardians of the fetuses, pregnant women are usually the first ones to find out whether the fetuses are abnormal. Therefore, the self-monitoring of pregnant women at home is an effective measure to prevent the occurrence of serious maternal and infant complications and further improve the quality of perinatal healthcare. At present, fetal heart monitoring has become one of the important fetal monitoring methods as well as the necessary means in the obstetrics department. The remote fetal monitoring system is a set of remote fetal heart rate transmission diagnostic systems based on a wireless network, which saves pregnant women the trouble of traveling to and from the hospital for fetal heart monitoring.

Factors such as umbilical cord compression, umbilical cord around the neck, intrauterine distress, intrauterine hypoxia, and abnormal fetal movement threaten the health of the fetuses all the time. The doctor needs to carry out an examination on fetal heart rate in order to promptly find out abnormal conditions and provide the treatment, so as to ensure the health of the fetuses and reduce fetal mortality. With 5G network, remote fetal heart rate monitoring can be completed by pregnant women at home, through which doctors can hear the fetal heart in real time and communicate with pregnant women through voice call, guide pregnant women to find the best location to hear fetal heart rate, promptly inform pregnant women of the monitoring results, and provide healthcare guidance (Fig. 2.12).

2.2.4 *Benefits for the disabled*

In terms of auxiliary artificial intelligence medical applications, 5G can add unlimited possibilities to the society through its network of greater stability. For example, apps for the visually impaired people such as Be My Eyes and Ariadne GPS can guide them to go out alone or even drive a car through voice maps. In such a complex outdoor environment, the instability of the network and the high delay will cause a delayed reaction, so the voice map will fail to give instructions in time, making it dangerous for the visually impaired users. With high speed and low delay by 5G network, such apps can give prompt location feedback, so as to avoid the occurrence of injuries and better serve the disabled.

58 *The World of 5G: Intelligent Medicine*

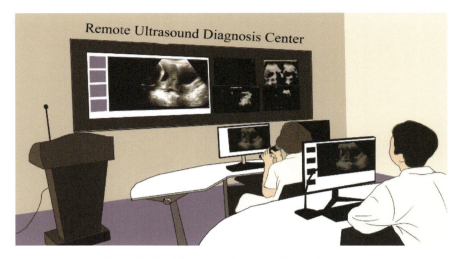

Figure 2.12 5G remote ultrasound diagnosis center.

5G technology helps people with visual and auditory defects through the use of Big Data, cloud computing, and other technologies. For example, the intelligent guide helmet, as a cloud wearable device, can provide high-precision real-time positioning navigation, path planning, obstacle avoidance, and other services to visually impaired people through enhanced cloud visual presentation. In addition, its leading hybrid intelligent services, such as face recognition, scene recognition, object recognition, and image classification, can help visually impaired people alleviate social impairments. Relying on the cloud intelligent technology, the intelligent guide helmet can help visually impaired people to recognize objects and sounds through voice commands and video collection uploaded to the cloud, so as to make up for the physical defects of visually impaired people.

In the future, the application of artificial intelligence in medical services will also be extended to robotic arms that know sign language, AI bionic limbs, etc., to help disabled people overcome the obstacles in life. However, when AI products enhance the real experience of disabled people, they need to rely on the support of a large amount of data and the real-time transmission of data. A robotic arm or an AI bionic limb could perform more elaborate actions with more tiny sensors, the support of mass data, and the high-speed and stable data transmission guaranteed by the 5G network. Services provided by medical products will be more intelligent and efficient with the powerful functions of both provided through the combination of AI technology and 5G network.

The highly sensitive robotic arm can assist the recovery of muscle strength after orthopedic surgery and the rehabilitation exercise of fine motor for people with Parkinson's disease and can effectively improve the self-care ability of patients. In addition, though with the continuous improvement of materials and structural processing technology, in the field of smart artificial limb, the flexibility and coordination of artificial limbs have greatly increased, yet in terms of the control of artificial limbs, the existing processors of smart artificial limbs, still controlled by the system, can merely recognize and react to the surrounding environment in a simple manner. The new theory suggests that by transmitting brain waves as electrical signals to the processors of smart artificial limbs, the user can autonomously control the artificial limbs, making disabled people deal with the complex environment around them in an easier way. The high density of 5G sensors on the bionic limbs makes it possible to regulate the artificial limbs freely with the brain waves. 5G+ AI bionic artificial limbs can also achieve more precise movements, which will greatly improve the quality of life of disabled people and build a healthier and more harmonious society.

Chapter 3

Better Healthcare within Your Reach

With the continuous development of the society, people have become more aware of their own health management, from the previous going to the hospital only when they're sick to the health management with regular exercise, active prevention, and regular physical examination in the hospital. The concept of health management is being gradually accepted by everyone. With the formal commercial use of 5G technology, personal health management and medical services will reach a new stage. Now, there are not only advanced instruments and equipment to monitor people's health in real time but also top-notch intelligent algorithms to help doctors arrive at a more accurate diagnosis. In the future, cutting-edge technologies such as the Internet+, Big Data, and artificial intelligence will be fully integrated and utilized in the medical and health field, and new health guardians will be created for everyone through products centering on 5G technology, through which smooth and unobstructed connection channels from health to illness, from hospital to family, and from doctor to patient can be constructed. Here is a brief introduction to some examples of the new momentum bestowed by 5G technology.

3.1 Intelligent Terminals Supported by 5G Technology

Generally speaking, the intelligent terminal is a kind of embedded computer system equipment, so its architecture frame is consistent with the embedded system structure. At the same time, as an application of the embedded system, its setting of application scenario is relatively clear.

62 The World of 5G: Intelligent Medicine

Therefore, its architecture is more explicit than the architecture of a common embedded system, with its granularity finer and with some characteristics of its own.

In recent years, many traditional medical device companies in the field of health care have chosen to cooperatively or independently develop new smart home health terminals. However, due to the limited technology and the failure in marketing, these attempts have not seen any good progress. The formal commercial use of 5G technology brings about an opportunity for the development of new health intelligent terminals. The super-high transmission of 5G can form the health Internet of Things through the effective connection of hardware and software of the health intelligent terminals.

The cloud of Big Data and artificial intelligence can provide more convenient conditions for data storage and software development. The following is the introduction of some current representative health intelligent terminals.

3.1.1 *Smart watches and smart bracelets*

Smart watches (Fig. 3.1) and smart bracelets are the members of the family of smart wearable devices, which is the general name of the wearable

Figure 3.1   Smart watch.

devices developed with intelligent designs by applying wearable technology to daily wearables.

Early smart watches were little more than timing tools with simple auxiliary calculation function. In 1994, Casio introduced VivCel VCL-100, a watch that could monitor incoming phone calls and alert users by vibrating, bringing the wristband closer to the phone. From 2000 to 2011, the exploration and improvement of smart devices has never stopped. However, in this period, the practicability of smart devices had been reduced due to various reasons such as large size, low expansibility, and high-power consumption, and the sales volume was not good.

In 2012, Pebble, a revolutionary product that was compatible with iOS and Android emerged with a sleek design, offered rich applications, and good scalability, which laid the foundation for health management through mobile devices, and soon attracted widespread attention after the sales went beyond one million. The successful launch of Apple Watch in 2014 pushed the wristband-style smart devices to a new climax and also firmly tied them to mobile phones. Currently, most smart watches allow users to add and remove apps at will to realize more functions.

Compared with smart watches, smart bracelets started much later, initially positioned as devices of small size, lightweight, and usefulness at low cost. The original intention of the smart bracelet is to detect the status of the users, with not many functions to record the exercise and diet of the users. The UP Generation wristband launched by Jawbone in 2011 appeared as the first wristband that monitored people's sleep quality, which gave people a surprise, but still couldn't change the fact that those wristbands were just pedometers. In 2013, with the rapid development of mobile communication and the Internet, Fitbit released their first smart bracelet. This smart bracelet not only added more sensors to monitor six body-related data but also innovatively developed the social properties of the smart bracelet, that is, it could realize data sharing through a supporting app, so that users can have a new group experience. However, due to the technical limitations of hardware and software, the development of smart bracelet has reached the bottleneck, which resulted in various companies still continuing to explore the future development of smart bracelets.

With the public's awareness of health management gradually strengthened and the deepened integration and application of cutting-edge technologies such as Big Data, cloud technology, and artificial intelligence under the promotion of 5G technology, each person's long-term health data will be brought into the new medical and health management mode, thus becoming the new guard of personal health management. For example, users' long-term health data such as heart rate, blood pressure, temperature, sleep time, and sleep quality can be dynamically monitored. Through Big Data analysis, users' health management can be suggested and even predicted to some extent. Dynamic real-time monitoring also enables timely contact with the patient's relatives at critical moments so that the patient can be sent to a doctor in time. By connecting to the cloud Big Data, health analysis reports can be generated for users periodically. These health data can help doctors better understand a patient's recent health when they visit a doctor. Health data is not only helpful for doctors to make a more accurate diagnosis and provide perfect treatment plans for the patients but also play a role in the study of the occurrence and development of some diseases.

At the same time, 5G technology plays as a bridge through which the hardware and software of smart wearable devices will be directly upgraded. Take heart rate monitoring as an example. At present, the smart bracelet generally carries out heart rate monitoring through PPG (photo plethysmography). Through relevant experiments, it can be concluded that the monitoring results in the static state are relatively consistent with the reality. However, when it comes to exercise, the monitoring results of many wearable smart bracelets will fluctuate to a certain extent. The smart bracelet can also offer the function of sleep monitoring. It analyzes sleep by monitoring the tiny movements of the body through a movement recorder, that is, measuring the sleep quality according to the range and frequency of wrist movement during sleep and judging whether the user is in the state of wakefulness, light sleep, or deep sleep.

However, for functions such as heart rate monitoring or sleep monitoring, the pre-set parameters of the smart wearable devices are needed in the process of health data feedback. Once the monitoring data is matched with the pre-set data, then the corresponding function will be triggered, and the smart bracelet will make a judgment on the user's current state. It can be concluded that the key to a more accurate judgment is the setting of the parameters, whose source depends on further research and analysis of Big Data.

Under the current data transmission conditions, users' health data, cloud health Big Data, and medical data of the medical institutions are relatively isolated, making it difficult to form a good contrast and direct interaction mode between the users and the medical institutions. Constrained by problems such as large volume, slow transmission, single transmission port, unsmoothness, as well as pending development of data application and analysis method, the maintenance and upgrade of software and hardware is still in the stage of slow development and the ability of prevention and treatment for emergencies are relatively weak. With the advent of the 5G era, the ultra-high transmission rate and extremely low delay will inevitably break down the barriers of interaction. Meanwhile, it will impact the existing chip and software market, drive a series of software and hardware upgrades, which will consequently enable smart wearable devices with timely feedback and adjustment. Moreover, with 5G as the link, some traditional smart wearable devices will surely take on new vitality and form a new health network together with other smart devices, contributing to the promotion of a new medical and health model.

3.1.2 *Intelligent medicine box*

In the 1990s, relevant experts put forward the concept of geotechnology in the first International Symposium on the Well-being of the Elderly held in the Netherlands, aiming to improve the living environment and experience of the elderly through technology centering on their actual needs. Year by year, the number of the elderly is increasing, most of whom suffer from chronic diseases, making the demand for drugs essential, and the medicine box for the storage of drugs a regular item for more and more families. At present, people use a medicine box merely for storage and convenient access of medicine, a function which a common medicine box can satisfy.

Most elderly relying on health care products or medicines often fail to take them regularly due to their poor memory, and in a few cases, children may take them by mistake. Considering this, the smart medicine box was developed. The early smart medicine box has simple functions such as safety lock and reminder for regular medication to solve the abovementioned problems, and at present, most of the smart medicine boxes in the market are of this kind. However, with the progress of science and technology, the new intelligent terminal of medical health is no longer limited to hospitals, but to conduct the monitoring of healthy people and the coverage of families. As an important part of Internet of Things for personal health management, the smart medicine box will gradually come into people's life. Thanks to 5G and Internet technology, the medicine box at home has got a "life" in itself. In the future, with the support of software and innovated technology, the smart medicine box will have following features:

3.1.2.1 Smart reminder

In addition to reminding you when to take the medicine, the smart medicine box will also remind you of the type and amount of the medicine you need to take and the present storage of the medicine. For example, information such as which drugs are in short supply and which drugs are about to exceed their expiration date will be timely recorded and presented at the smart terminal. For the elderly with cardiovascular and cerebrovascular diseases and others with long-term medication needs, customized medication plans will be made and be adjusted regularly with suggestions given. These functions also depend on the further integration of 5G, Big Data, cloud computing, and other modules. The intelligent terminals, with the sound interaction with the user's personal health data through new algorithms by connecting the cloud data through 5G technology, will safeguard their health in a new way.

3.1.2.2 Guardian system

For those who are busy with work and concerned about their parents' health at home, the smart medicine box can also serve as a bridge of family affection connecting family members. With the support of 5G, people can connect their smart phones to their parents' smart medicine boxes at home through supporting apps, so as to monitor their parents' medication more conveniently and keep an eye on their medication at anytime and anywhere. People will also get timely feedback if their parents fail to take their medication on time. The medication records generated periodically through the supporting app can be stored as cloud data for easy reference at anytime, providing the basis for the adjustment of subsequent medication. In addition, the smart medicine box also offers the function of one-press call. When in an emergency, the sharp change of vital signs of the elderly can activate the medicine box immediately and make phone calls or send emergency information to their families, so as to buy more time for saving their lives.

3.1.2.3 *Telemedicine*

With the advent of 5G technology, ultra-high speed and ultra-low latency have facilitated remote consultations. Through the supporting app, the elderly can enjoy regular remote consultation or telemedicine consultation service through the connection between the smart medicine box and the hospital by mobile phone or computer without leaving their home, which is not only conducive to timely discovering their own health problems but also saves the journey to the hospital and the time for registration, thanks to the convenience of telemedicine under 5G.

3.1.3 *Intelligent blood pressure monitor*

The smart sphygmomanometer, differing from the traditional sphygmomanometer, can upload the measured blood pressure data to the cloud, measure and record the user's blood pressure in real time, or automatically through a variety means of transmission, such as Bluetooth, USB (Universal Serial Bus) or GPRS (General Packet Radio Service), to analyze the changes in blood pressure with Big Data and conduct timely detection, warning, and analysis of the blood pressure data of elderly users.

Currently, most smart sphygmomanometers offer many more functions, such as reminding users of medication and exercises on time, in case they forget to. Some also offer health counseling, which can be done in the software that comes with the smart sphygmomanometer. Some of the features are similar to other smart devices, but the biggest advantage of smart sphygmomanometers is that they can accurately measure the user's blood pressure, so it's a good choice for home use. In addition, the historical data uploaded to the cloud can be used to establish a permanent health record for users. In the future medical treatment process, the data of users' health status can be exported for analysis, statistics, and report, so as to provide a reference for doctors to make diagnosis and treatment plans. The smart sphygmomanometer can instantly get and track the user's health status, carry out disease prevention and control, and also help to realize the new mode of intelligent medical management for health and disease.

3.1.4 *Ambulance*

"The patient appears to have a ruptured spleen and pleural effusion".

"Real-time data of the patient received from the patient, ready for surgery".

68 The World of 5G: Intelligent Medicine

This is a dialogue between a 5G ambulance simulating the first aid task and the directing center of a hospital in Chongqing. In the directing center of the hospital, experts give remote guidance of first aid according to the situation of patients in the ambulance and arrange follow-up work quickly to buy precious time for lives. With its technical advantages of high speed, low delay, wide connection, and good stability, 5G has laid an expressway for saving lives (from chinanews.com).

Since the second half of 2019, many hospitals and communication companies in several provinces and cities in China have cooperated to apply 5G technology to emergency ambulances (Fig. 3.2), which can send patients' basic information and data back to the hospital in real time. In the future, hospitals and communication companies will build a comprehensive medical emergency system based on 5G ambulances and artificial intelligence, augmented reality (AR)/virtual reality (VR), and other applications. When a patient in a critical condition gets on a 5G ambulance, the accompanying doctor can complete a series of examinations such as blood test, electrocardiogram, and ultrasound immediately with

Figure 3.2 Ambulance.

5G medical equipment before transmitting more information such as medical images, patient signs, and condition records to the hospital in real time through the 5G network. Experts in the directing center of the hospital can also use AR/VR equipment to guide the rescue of critical patients "on site" and fully understand the patient's detailed conditions, so as to make a quick rescue plan and make preparation for the operation in advance. This enables patients to be hospitalized from the moment they get into the ambulance through the seamless linkage between outside and inside the hospital, greatly shortening the rescue response time and striving for greater chances for the health of the patients.

3.2 AR/VR Applications Driven by 5G

AR (augmented reality) technology can be traced back to the 1950s and 1960s. Through the application of multimedia, three-dimensional (3D) modeling, real-time tracking and registration, intelligent interaction, sensing, and other technical means, after 3D registration of the known real environment information, the computer-generated text, images, 3D models, music, videos, and other virtual information will be integrated into the real world, so as to deepen the user's understanding of the real world through the "enhancement" of the real world by complementation between the two kinds of information.

Proposed in the 1980s, the concept of VR (virtual reality) refers to the technology that realizes human interaction with computers, various sensors, and image display technology, and it is defined as the product of a cross combination of computer interaction, image computing, artificial intelligence, and sensing technology. Featuring immersion, interaction, and imagination, VR enables users with a multi-sensory immersive experience through electronic components.

AR and VR are two hot technologies nowadays, but people have been exploring them in the medical field for a long time. In 1989, the National Library of the United States launched the Digital Human Engineering Project, which was aimed at realizing the digitization and visualization of the human body in all aspects. In 2006, under the support of the National 863 Program and the leadership of Mr. Zhong Shizhen, a senior academician of the Chinese Academy of Engineering, China completed the "China Digital Man No. 1", becoming the third country after the United States and South Korea to have the model of a digital human, which laid the foundation for the development of digital medicine and the application of

AR/VR technology. In recent years, with the progress of science and technology, more and more attempts and applications of AR/VR technology in the medical field emerged. In November 2018, the Xi'an Children's Hospital successfully completed the first domestic AR-assisted resection of intracranial vascular malformation for a child.

Zheng Minhua, the director of general surgery department of Shanghai Ruijin Hospital, and his team completed the first domestic live broadcast of 5G+ VR surgery on the eve of the official commercial use of 5G. The year 2020 marked the first year of 5G in the real sense. In this year, 5G was officially commercialized, which provided the application of AR/VR technology to cope with larger data volume with ultra-high transmission rate and ultra-low delay. Let's learn about some innovations that may be applied in the field of medicine and health in the future.

3.2.1 *Virtual teaching platform based on augmented reality (AR)/virtual reality (VR)*

Walter Greenleaf, the director of Stanford's VR Medical Research Institute, is one of the world's pioneers who applied virtual reality in medicine. As an authority in the industry, he believes that the combination of VR and medicine can be applied in the following four aspects: medical training, clinical diagnosis and treatment, medical intervention, and health care. Next, upon the following examples, we will discuss the virtual teaching platform based on AR/VR.

Generally, medical colleges are faced with the conflict between the increasing number of students and relative lack of medical training resources. As cradles for life engineers, it is very important to improve their teaching quality. For medical institutions, in clinical practice, junior doctors are the reserve force of every hospital, and they often need to complete a large amount of accumulation through contact with clinical cases, so as to take charge in the future. The popularization and application of AR/VR and 5G technologies will provide new solutions to these problems. These solutions are provided as follows:

(1) *Experimental lectures*: Taking the experiment course of human anatomy as an example, as a basic introductory course that medical students must learn, the course of human anatomy is the key to enter the medical world. Limited by the number of human body specimens, students can only use the specimen in a one-to-many or even many-to-many way in the teaching process, which will only facilitate the

students with a simple understanding and exploration of the human body. In addition, due to the limited classroom time, some students often fail to get a systematic understanding in class at the end of the course; besides, no deep impression can be left in the students' minds for they cannot operate with their own hands in the class. The AR/VR technology can help realize the one-to-one learning mode for students, who will have multidimensional cognition through the decomposition and touch of specimens. It will also help to avoid the consumption of human specimens, while enhancing their memory. Because the anatomical structure of human body is very complex, which contains a very large amount of data, and AR/VR equipment is very expensive at present, many companies propose to build a separate AR/VR classroom for schools (Fig. 3.3).

After the application of 5G, large-scale data transmission would be easier so as to facilitate the acquisition and update of data. With the increasing popularity of AR/VR devices, students can study anytime and anywhere on the campus of colleges and universities in the future.

(2) *Theory class*: Most of the time, medical students are confined to books, where they see flat things, but not three-dimensionally. These

Figure 3.3   VR classroom.

materials are unable to generate interaction, and the dull text cannot stimulate students' interest. By using AR/VR technology, part of the content can be presented directly (Fig. 3.4). For example, medical students can get familiar with the entire surgical process of the hospital in the virtual scene, and relatively complex structures and organs can be decomposed and comprehensively displayed, which can help medical students grasp the anatomical structure relationship more quickly.

In addition, the AR/VR technology can also help reduce the cost of teaching. In 2016 and 2018, the AR/VR elements was used in *3D Systematic Anatomy* and the ninth edition of medical materials published by the People's Medical Publishing House. In the ninth edition of the medical textbooks, the pictures in the book will be presented in three dimensions when scanned through the relevant

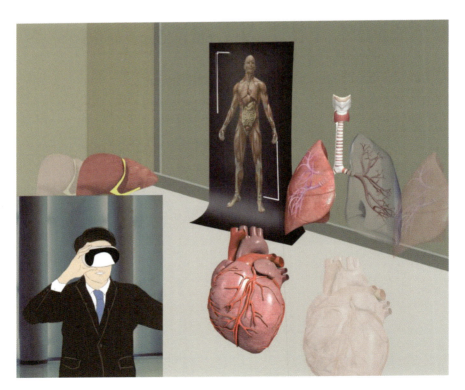

Figure 3.4 3D systematic anatomy.

smartphone apps. The original plain black and white pictures would be converted into 3D color images, with capillaries and others clearly seen. By changing their angles, students can distinguish the structures as if they were seeing real objects.

(3) *Clinical diagnosis and treatment*: AR/VR technology can help junior doctors in hospitals to understand the operating path of various surgeries and improve their surgical skills rapidly. Excellent surgical cases can be shared through the integration of AR/VR technology and 5G technology. Experts can also conduct remote operations using AR/VR technology. However, remote surgery has a high demand on detection technology and different real-time feedback for different operations and the 5G technology to provide ultra-low delay, so as to eliminate the influence of the physical distance between the remote detection of the doctors and the patients as well as to realize real-time detection thousands of miles away and provide a strong guarantee for the operation.

3.2.2 *VR ward visits*

The VR ward visit, as an application of VR technology in remote communication and interaction, presents a good solution for people who cannot visit the patient ward for various reasons, or patients who have high requirements for the treatment environment so that a close visit is not supported. Although some hospitals have taken the lead in VR ward visits, they have not had a good experience due to the limited transmission speed. With the popularization of VR devices and the application of 5G technology, this new visiting mode will gradually become the mainstream. VR ward visits can not only break the regional restrictions but also save time and unnecessary expenses for patients and their relatives as well as improve patients' environmental experience. Patients and visitors can communicate with each other by wearing VR devices, so that both parties can have an "immersive" experience. This also reflects the humanistic care of modern medicine.

In May 2019, the Jinan Maternity and Child Health Hospital and the West China Second Hospital of Sichuan University took the lead in opening a 5G+ VR newborn visiting system. Hospitals across the country have followed suit, opening similar visitation systems ahead of 2020. It can be predicted that after 5G is officially commercialized, the application prospect of this new visitation system will be broader.

3.3 5G+ AI Diagnosis: 5G Can Meet Your Urgent Needs

AI refers to the theory, method, technology, and application system used to simulate and extend human intelligence. It was first coined in 1956, when a group of young scientists, including McCasey and Minsky, came up with the term of artificial intelligence while discussing how machines could be used to simulate intelligence. In 1997, the supercomputer Deep Blue beat the chess world champion Kasparov with 11.38 billion floating-point calculations per second, demonstrating the super computing power of computers while also making people more optimistic about the future of artificial intelligence. Until a few years ago, after a long period of accumulation, artificial intelligence finally ushered in its own development. Demis Hassabis' team at Google DeepMind had developed a deep learning artificial intelligence program called AlphaGo. In 2016, the program defeated the world champion Go player Lee Sedol, who is also a professional ninth dan, with the score of 4 to 1. In 2017, the program defeated the then world No. 1 Go player Ke Jie with the score of 3 to 0. Artificial intelligence (AI) became famous all of a sudden and caught the attention of the world again.

In recent years, artificial intelligence has developed in all fields, and it is no exception in the medical field, especially in the diagnosis of diseases, which has made preliminary achievements. With the support of 5G technology, 5G+ AI diagnostics will certainly play a big role. Let's take a look at what AI can do in terms of disease diagnosis.

3.3.1 *Intelligent diagnosis of skin diseases*

We often emphasize that early detection, early diagnosis, and early treatment are necessary for diseases. But many diseases tend to occur insidiously in the early stage. The characteristics of them are not obvious, and they are not very recognizable and are easy to be ignored. On the one hand, the initial symptoms of the disease are relatively mild, coupled with the indifference of many patients, and it takes a lot of time to go to the hospital to see a doctor, so that patients are reluctant to go to the hospital to see a doctor. These tend to lead to the neglect of diseases. On the other hand, the hospital receives a large number of patients every day, so doctors have a high workload. There is also the possibility of misdiagnosis and error diagnosis.

These two factors have become an obstacle to the early diagnosis of the disease. In the case of skin diseases, there are about 5.4 million new cases of skin cancer each year in the United States, with malignant tumors accounting for 20% of the total. Although melanoma accounts for only 5% of skin malignancies, it is associated with 75% of skin deaths, which is more than 10,000 skin deaths a year. If diagnosed early, the five-year survival rate is more than 99%, compared sharply with 14% of survival rate in patients with advanced melanoma. So, the question is how do you diagnose early melanomas that look similar to moles without obvious symptoms? At present, by using artificial intelligence algorithms such as disease classification and individual mapping method to build deep learning networks, doctors and patients can actively track skin diseases and find early-stage cancers through images.

In early attempts, due to constraints such as insufficient data and that the data cannot be standardized, the work of computer-aided skin disease diagnosis and classification could not reach the diagnosis level of the doctor. A traditional dermoscopy examination is conducted by utilizing specialized optical instruments, and histopathological images are obtained through invasive biopsies and microscopic examination. All these methods of image acquisition need to be acquired by professional equipment, which is not conducive to the extensive promotion and application of an auxiliary diagnostic system. Therefore, if there is a method to realize an auxiliary diagnosis with ordinary images, this method will be of great significance for auxiliary diagnosis of skin diseases. However, variable factors such as zoom, angle, and illumination pose great challenges to the stability and accuracy of the auxiliary system. Thus, some scholars place their hopes on artificial intelligence to assist the diagnosis and make it a method to overcome data variability through training based on Big Data.

Many existing methods require a large number of pretreatments, lesion segmentation, and extraction of specific visual features in the domain before classification diagnosis, which have very high requirements for professional operations. Moreover, the amount of data is relatively small (usually only about 1,000 cases), and the generalization of data is greatly compromised. However, with the development and progress of technology, the new technology and system do not need manual tags, but can directly use a network to train the image tags and raw pixels, thus greatly reducing the workload.

At present, a number of institutions and hospitals at home and abroad have been cooperating with each other to conduct further research to improve the skin AI diagnosis. The formal commercial use of 5G technology further expands the application space of AI diagnosis, and more scholars, R&D personnel, and commercial institutions are focusing on this field. The ultra-high transmission speed, huge capacity, and more reliable data of 5G will open the door to AI diagnosis for thousands upon thousands of families. It is hoped that in the near future, people will only need to send a photo to complete the diagnosis of skin diseases.

In 2017, Andre Esteva, Brett Kuprel, Roberto A Novoa, Sebastian Thrun *et al.* from the Stanford University developed an intelligent skin-assisted diagnosis system using the deep convolutional neural network. The system used 129,450 skin images and corresponding labels to complete the training, covering 2,032 common skin diseases. The diagnostic labels are obtained by dermatologists based on the results of dermoscopy or histological images. In the clinical trial, AI's diagnosis was compared with that of 21 medical practitioners, and AI's diagnosis was similar to or even slightly better than that of the doctors.

In 2019, Google AI recognition launched a diagnostic system that can assist in the diagnosis of 26 skin diseases, with an accuracy rate of about 90%, comparable to that of a senior expert.

After summarizing more than 3,750 cases to obtain the true label, AI was able to diagnose the top 1 and top 3 in the list of common skin diseases with an accuracy rate of 71% and 93%, respectively.

In addition, by comparing the diagnostic accuracy of AI with that of three types of clinicians (dermatologists, general practitioners, and interns), it can be found that the diagnostic accuracy of AI reaches 90%, which is completely superior to the diagnostic accuracy of 75% of dermatologists, 60% of general practitioners, and 55% of interns.

In addition, the system especially tested for different skin colors. When the subjects were of different skin colors, the AI's diagnostic accuracy rate for top one of common skin diseases ranged from 69% to 72%, and the AI's diagnostic accuracy rate for top three of common skin diseases ranged from 91% to 94%. Therefore, the system would not make misjudgments due to the difference of skin color.

3.3.2 *AI can diagnose eye diseases*

The eye is the window of the soul and the most important sensory organ of the human body. As an important part of the visual system, the eye is responsible for the acquisition and processing of raw information.

The importance of eye health, identified by the World Health Organization as one of the three major problems of human quality of life, can be seen from this. The quality of eyesight has a direct relationship with the health of the eyes, which has a substantial impact on people's life and work quality.

A very small number of visual impairments are caused by congenital causes, and most are developed by various factors acquired after birth. The latter can be avoided. An analysis of 61 items of visual impairment data from 35 countries showed that uncorrected ametropia, cataracts, and retinopathy are the most common causes of visual impairment and that uncorrected ametropia is the second leading cause of blindness. Myopia is a kind of ametropia. Patients have hyperrefractive lenses and cornea, and the axis of the eye is too long, so that light is imaged in front of the retina, leading to normal near vision and loss of distant vision. Early myopia, if not treated, is likely to develop into high myopia, and high myopia brings very easily serious fundus change, which may develop into pathological myopia and cause irreversible visual impairment and even blindness.

Children's heavy learning tasks and pressure, the increasing use of electronic products which leads to excessive eye use, and poor eye hygiene are all potential risk factors for myopia. The current findings suggest that the prevalence of myopia and high myopia will increase significantly globally and that the total number of moderate or severe visual impairment and blindness due to uncorrected myopia will increase significantly as the population ages and the world population grows. In fact, most fundus oculi diseases have a definite treatment window, and timely screening of fundus oculi diseases can effectively reduce unnecessary vision loss. The primary test method for myopia is the diopter test.

At present, the traditional measurement of diopter can be divided into the following two categories: objective measurement and subjective measurement. Objective measurement does not require patient feedback, but results are obtained through relevant optometry instruments and methods, such as machine detection of myopia degree. The subjective test is based on the patient's subjective judgment and the results are obtained through the corresponding optometric instruments. For example, the doctor tests the patient's general vision level through the visual acuity chart. Both tests can only produce good results with qualified ophthalmologists and optometric instruments. For parents who care about their children, it would be much more convenient if there is a convenient way to check their children's eyesight regularly.

At present, some institutions in China are trying to introduce machine learning methods to study the automatic prediction of refraction and automatic diagnosis of pathological myopia. It can promptly diagnose the diopter without the use of optometric instruments, assist doctors to make effective correction, or give treatment prescriptions. It can also be effective in prompt screening of pathological myopia and then assist doctors in the prevention and control of patients' ocular fundus pathology in advance and play the role of remote auxiliary medicine in certain circumstances.

Now we can imagine, in the near future, whether people will be able to do this examination with 5G and home VR devices? At home, the patient uses a wearable VR device to simulate different scenes under the guidance of a doctor. Then, the AI uses the machine to observe and record the changes in the patient's retina, lens, and fundus to predict the changes in eye refraction in the future and uploads the patient data with pathological trends to the cloud via the 5G network so that the doctors and patients can observe the patient's condition in the future. The whole process is relaxed and pleasant, which can provide a strong basis for disease prevention and treatment while promptly treating the patient's disease.

3.3.3 *Accurate analysis of brain diseases*

Intracranial tumors have always been a disease with high mortality due to the particularity of its tumor location. In order to improve the survival rate and prolong the survival cycle of patients, radiologists need to develop personalized surgery and treatment plan according to the disease situation of patients with intracranial tumors. Generally speaking, the overall operation and treatment plan for intracranial tumors should be customized according to the type and level of intracranial tumors suffered by patients, so this requires an early and accurate diagnosis of intracranial tumors.

Currently, the early diagnosis of intracranial tumors and the location of the lesions are manually analyzed by radiologists based on the medical images of the patients. As the training of a good radiologist and manual analysis are both time-consuming and labor-intensive, manual analysis relies heavily on the radiologist's personal experience. Therefore, it is particularly important to develop an AI system for automatic diagnosis and mass segmentation of intracranial tumors that can assist radiologists in analyzing tumor types and location. Targeted drugs are one of the ways to treat tumors, and genetic defects in patients with intracranial tumors are usually determined by gene sequencing. However, due to its high cost, most hospitals do not provide gene sequencing testing. Generally speaking, genes determine traits, so tumor traits in medical imaging are determined by genetic defects. Meanwhile, the characteristics of intracranial tumors in imaging can also reflect genetic defects to a certain extent. So not only can AI diagnostic systems help doctors make diagnoses more efficiently, it may also be possible in the future to automatically analyze areas of intracranial tumors in medical images to identify genetic defects.

In recent years, medical image-assisted analysis based on deep learning technology has gradually become a research hotspot. More and more studies show that, compared with the traditional manual analysis method, deep learning technology has great advantages in the fields of pattern recognition, semantic image segmentation, and feature representation. Deep learning techniques generally use deep neural networks, such as convolutional neural networks, to automatically extract high-level feature representations of images and complete tasks such as recognition and classification, predictive regression, semantic segmentation, and so on through multilevel features. In general, the combination of GPU (graphics processing unit and graphics processor) auxiliary analysis tools to accelerate technology deep learning can be dealt with within 1 s of thousands of images and through the multilayer neural network to extract what the naked eye cannot observe, which is subtle image characteristics, and with the increase of the number of cases of processing, deep learning auxiliary analysis precision is improved. Therefore, compared with the traditional low efficiency and low accuracy of the manual analysis method, the deep learning assisted analysis tool has the advantages of high efficiency, high accuracy, and not relying on the diagnostic experience of radiologists, which greatly reduces the workload of radiologists and improves their working efficiency. In addition, deep learning technology can also assist radiologists in completing some tasks that cannot be completed manually, such as image compensation and 3D reconstruction.

However, building such a sophisticated, complex AI system is fraught with difficulties. Being responsible for life and health, the AI system not only calls for more precise and accurate algorithms to reduce errors but also needs enough data of the patient cases to support its development. At the same time, this process should be fed back to the researchers for systematic improvement and correction. It is a long battle against diseases. At present, most of the research is being carried out through the mutual cooperation between hospitals and universities or scientific research institutions. However, the limitation of location and data volume hinders the progress of research. If the study has enough cases and enough geographical distribution, it can be more effective with less effort. The official commercial use of 5G technology gives such research a glimmer of hope. With 5G technology, a number of hospitals and scientific research institutions can realize the communication of large amounts of data in a very short time and track the follow-up progress of the disease in combination with the cloud storage technology currently under development, so as to truly realize the all-round observation of diagnosis, treatment, and prognosis.

Chapter 4

5G-Pioneered Robust Healthcare for the Future

5G is both a bridge and a platform, providing a path and a space for new technologies, new methods, and new models to be connected and integrated into the field of healthcare. Meanwhile, it is also a catalyst to make many ideas of scientists easier to realize. It can be said that the arrival of 5G will certainly set off a new storm in the field of medicine and healthcare, which makes us full of expectations for the new medical and health model in the future. In the following sections, let's analyze briefly how 5G will change the medical field.

4.1 Easy Access to Famous Doctors at Any Time

4.1.1 *Holographic projection: A new mode of medical interaction*

Compared to the 4G network, the 5G network not only has a higher transmission rate but also presents characteristics of low delay, high reliability, and low power consumption during transmission, which can better support the application of Internet of Things and greatly promote holographic projection technology. With the continuous progress of projection technology, holographic projection has gradually come in the public eye and is gradually being applied in many fields. Holographic projection technology brings obvious changes to many industries. By using holographic projection technology, the catering industry can combine an elegant restaurant atmosphere with delicious food to create a medley of vision and taste. The cultural tourism industry can arrange such realistic novel scenes that people can't distinguish between reality and projection. The education sector can build more vivid three-dimensional multi-functional exhibition halls. The healthcare industry can, by dissecting the diseased body, produce fine images in which even blood vessels can be distinguished.

In 2012, researchers at the Human Media Lab at Queen's University of Canada successfully developed a 3D holographic projection device called TeleHuman. The system consists of a 1.8-meter-tall cylinder with a built-in 3D projector and six self-moving sensors mounted on top of the cylinder. After the camera captures the image, the computer would form a 3D hologram according to the image and render it on the cylinder. The cylinder has a 360° angle of view and participants of the video conference can walk around it. To demonstrate that the holographic projection system is interactive, the researchers used an app on TeleHuman called BodiPod, which can build a 3D anatomical model of the human body. Through simple gestures, the app can perform complex operations such as cutting open the human skin and we can directly observe muscles, nerves, and bone structure. This undoubtedly brings hope for the application of holographic projection in the education of the medical industry and even the operation of telemedicine surgery.

TeleHuman 2 followed in 2018. Compared to the first-generation product, the new product can realize interaction through naked vision and projection without glass-like devices. In addition, users can walk around the device and see the images from different visual angles. It's the world's first 3D holographic video conferencing system.

In 2013, RealViewIging, an Israeli company, developed a set of holographic projection technology and interface systems. In cooperation with Philips Health, it combined 3D holographic projection with interventional heart disease, making a meaningful attempt for the application of holographic projection technology in the medical field. Through an image database derived from the health system, doctors can directly control images, including zoom in, zoom out, mark, and turn in circles, by using a stylus or hands and can connect a computer with a transformational X-ray detector to give a clear real-time projection of the certain organ or blood vessels.

Elhanan Bruckheimer, an Israeli surgeon, said that "This new system can provide anatomy maps of the human body, and it's very realistic.

The doctor can see everything about the body's tissues, including where the organs are and how the body works. With its help, you can perform surgery better and better understand the structure of the body". The system also allows doctors to see and analyze the heart more clearly in 3D instead of 2D, and doctors can even penetrate it, touch it, and observe its interaction with the surrounding tissues (Fig. 4.1). Bruckheimer also said, "With this new technique, the success rate of surgery will be greatly improved".

In addition to reducing the doctor's time wastage and the amount of radiation a patient is exposed to during an exam, holographic projection technology can also be used to project a patient's body parts into a specific location via a projection device in the form of suspension. The combination of holographic projection technology and medical care is the equivalent of putting a visible heart into the hands of a surgeon who can get all information about the heart in all-round and real-time display. The convenience and realism of 3D holographic projection systems, which can produce real images while doctors wear no special glasses, allow the new technology to be useful even in minimally invasive surgery. Until now, most paramedical tests, such as CT or MRI, which are widely used, have provided the surgeon with only 2D images. In addition to the field of repairing or replacing heart valves, many non-visual minimally invasive operations (such as endoscopic exploration and puncture) have great application prospects. In addition, in practical applications (such as the examination of the spatial relationship between blood vessels and nerves),

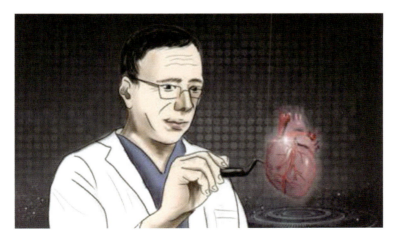

Figure 4.1 Holographic projection of the heart.

holographic projection technology is beneficial in reducing unnecessary injuries to organs or blood vessels.

However, to better meet the clinical needs, holographic projection with clearer images is also required by doctors. The structure of the human body is very complex, thus, in order to realize remote consultation through holographic projection in the future, a high-resolution instrument is essential. For such a huge amount of data, how to achieve storage and fast transmission is also a big problem at present.

In the past era of the 4G network, technology enables us to realize instant video communication on mobile phone terminals. As a new generation of mobile communication networks, the 5G network can theoretically transmit at a rate of 10 Gb/s, which increases the transmission rate by 10 times and brings more possibilities for communication. On this basis, meetings of many companies of the terminal industry will appear as shown in Fig. 4.2. 3D video calling, which only appears in science fiction movies, will also enter people's daily work and life.

Take OPPO as an example. The 3D video calling technology based on 5G network developed by OPPO is hoped to make full use of the characteristics of 5G network, such as high speed, low delay, and wide connection, to support the transmission of 3D Big Data and to further display the traditional 2D video calling in a 3D stereoscopic environment, which is called holographic projection by us.

The rapid development of communication technology combining light structure and 5G network is bound to bring earth-shaking changes to

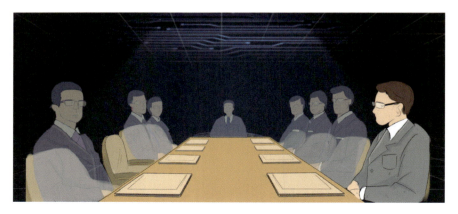

Figure 4.2   Video conference with holographic projection.

people's lives, which would be reflected in the fact that many people far away from home can have face-to-face video calls with their loved ones in close proximity, and for people of all industries, it is also an immersive meeting experience. In the medical field, for example, video conferencing conveys too little information, so expert consultation often requires doctors to participate in the collection and analysis of patients' conditions on the spot, while the arrival of holographic projection meetings can enable doctors to directly conduct remote consultation. The information of patients' condition could be transmitted to the experts attending the meeting in the way of 3D stereoscopic projection, which not only can reduce the burden of doctors but also can improve the utilization rate of medical resources and enable experts to diagnose and treat patients more effectively.

4.1.2 *Famous doctors gather and Big Data helps you diagnose the disease*

At present, most medical data usually exists in the physical form, including medical records, expense lists, doctor's written medical records, prescriptions, and imaging data. The electronic archive is only available in the hospital where the patient is treated. Once the hospital is changed, the patient will face a lot of inconvenience.

With the improvement of people's living standards and consumption levels as well as the gradual improvement of medical services, the personal medical data of patients is growing rapidly, which also leads to the inevitable demand for the simplification and miniaturization of medical data. With the rapid development of science and technology, powerful data storage devices, computers, and the Internet have been developed and popularized, which provides a new way for mass medical data storage: electronic digitization.

The development of 5G technology brings opportunities for electronic digitization of medical resources, and the fast data transmission speed provides conditions for the sharing of medical data. Storage capacity is higher than ever. The improvement of transmission security guarantees the security of citizens' personal privacy. The lower transmission cost ensures the feasibility of its promotion and implementation.

Medical data, such as medical records and medical images, is converted to digital form in varying degrees and stored in electronic devices.

86 *The World of 5G: Intelligent Medicine*

The cross-field application of technologies in the fields of mobile Internet, Big Data, and cloud computing in the medical field enables the emerging technologies and new service models to quickly penetrate into all aspects of the medical industry (Figs. 4.3 and 4.4).

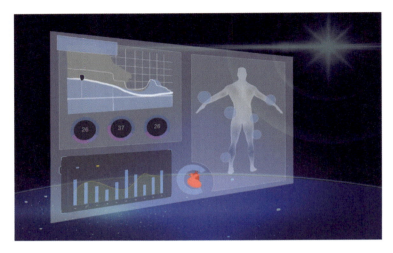

Figure 4.3   Data panel renderings.

Figure 4.4   Imaginary diagram of medical care under Big Data.

In the traditional medical diagnosis mode, doctors can only diagnose by relying on the limited patient information collected as well as their own experience and knowledge reserve, which brings great limitations to clinical diagnosis and decision-making. If the medical image data, medical records, examination results, and medical service costs of patients are input into the Big Data system, the etiology and treatment plan of patients with similar symptoms can be obtained through machine learning and mining analysis. This can not only provide a reference for doctors' clinical decision-making but also greatly improve the accuracy of diagnosis.

At present, the new digital transformation trend of the medical and health industry is mainly to break the limitations of information isolation between hospitals and departments under the traditional medical mode through medical Internet of Things, medical cloud, medical Big Data application, and many other information technologies, so as to achieve effective coordination and complementation between all parties.

In 2016, Wuzhou made full use of Big Data technology and took the lead in the planning and design of the "national health information platform" at the prefecture level in Guangxi. It invested more than 46 million yuan to build the national health information platform at the municipal level. Through electronic carriers such as electronic health cards, electronic medical records, and electronic health records for residents, it realized information interconnection and mutual recognition and resource sharing among all kinds of medical and health institutions in the city, in order to eliminate the "information islands" caused by problems such as medical information is not shared and medical data systems between hospitals are not matched, which greatly improves the quality of medical service.

In terms of residents' health monitoring, the new service model of "Internet+ medical and health" is booming. The promotion and application of Big Data in healthcare have provided help for people to seek medical service, monitor residents' health status, and prevent and control diseases. Through the application of Big Data technology, residents' health records, including all medical information and clinical decisions, can be collected and provided, and more accurate treatment plans can be provided for sick residents, making the treatment process closer to accurate treatment. For healthy people, Big Data technology can integrate relevant information, analyze the factors threatening the health of residents through the data of the incidence, and mortality and causes of various local diseases, so as to carry out targeted prevention and popularization of science. Now, the Big Data of residents' health released every year across the country is the product of the application of Big Data technology.

In her book *The Patient Revolution: How Big Data and Analytics Are Transforming the Health Care Experience*, Krisa Taylor makes this point, "In the future, the medical industry will become a service industry, and the relationship between doctors and individuals will no longer be the relationship between doctors and patients, but the service relationship between all medical resources and each individual with healthcare needs. Individuals will become customers and consumers of the medical industry, and all resources will be built around them".

If the personalized healthcare of Big Data mentioned by Krisa Taylor is realized, a huge medical data inventory will be generated accordingly. Behind this massive medical data, the development of corresponding data transmission technology is needed. In the 4G era, with the continuous rise of data scale, the pressure of data transmission and storage is increasing. In view of the scale and speed of 4G data transmission, it is more about the development of interpersonal connections, such as video conferencing.

In the age of 5G, 5G not only improves the speed of the network but also makes up for the shortcoming of the development of Big Data and artificial intelligence. In the 5G environment, AI can provide faster response speed, richer information content, smarter application mode, and more intuitive user experience, thus giving birth to new application scenarios such as medical image analysis, health management, and disease prediction. Thanks to the characteristics of 5G with high speed and low delay as well as the platform capability of Big Data analysis, the connection between things and the connection between people and things has been developed into the Internet of Things. The diversification of data terminals makes the acquisition of Big Data more complicated and the data types more diverse.

The application of Big Data, cloud storage, MEC (Mobile Edge Computing), artificial intelligence, and other technologies has greatly improved work efficiency and realized better configuration and utilization of medical resources. The development of 5G will improve the service capacity of mobile medical units and solve the problem of increasing demand for medical resources.

It can be predicted that 5G+ Big Data medical treatment is the future trend. The application of these two technologies is leading us to precision medicine and intelligent medicine. But to be really accurate, on the one hand, we need to really dig out the connotation of all the medical Big Data; on the other hand, it is necessary to constantly strengthen the understanding of the whole medical Big Data and use the advantages of 5G technology in the Internet of Things to increase the knowledge reserve of the computer so that it can classify similar medical records and provide practical help for doctors to make clinical decisions. Of course, the existing AI system may also need to be improved. We have seen the difficulties to be overcome in the analysis of medical Big Data, but we should also see the hope it brings to us. It is a technology that can comprehensively improve the quality of medical services and bring tremendous changes to the treatment of patients.

4.2 Complex Operation Can be Simply Done

4.2.1 *By utilizing AR/VR technology, full view without dead angle can be realized*

As a new technology with high popularity in recent years, VR technology has been widely applied in various fields, and the medical field is naturally one of its key application fields. In 2015, psychiatrists at the University of Louisville in the United States used VR technology to help patients overcome phobias for the first time, creating a controlled simulation environment for claustrophobic patients, so that patients can overcome avoidance psychology to face their own fears. Furthermore, you can use this technique to practice coping strategies. The simulated world is private and secure.

In the U.S. state of Texas, a professor called Dallas has created a training program to help autistic children learn social skills. This project uses brain imaging and brain wave monitoring technology to present children's common learning, social interaction, and work situations through VR technology, so that they can understand the society, make their emotional expression easier to be recognized by the society, and help them better integrate into the society. Using brain scans, Dallas found that children with autism improved their ability to understand society after being trained in virtual reality.

After the popularity of VR technology, AR technology has gradually come into the public's eyes. Compared to VR technology replacing the real world, AR technology is to add virtual objects in the real space.

Data show that in recent years, AR technology has been more mature in the application of the commercial medical field, especially in medical plastic surgery, cosmetology, and minimally invasive surgery. A start-up company, ILLUSIO, from California, USA, officially used AR in preoperative consulting for plastic surgery according to patient needs.

AR technology can not only effectively reflect the real-world content but also promote the display of virtual information content. These delicate contents complement and overlay each other. In visual augmented reality, the helmet-mounted display enables the real world to overlap with the computer graphics, after which the real world can be clearly seen around the helmet-mounted display. In AR technology, there are mainly new technologies and means such as multimedia, 3D modeling, and scene fusion. There are obvious differences between the information content provided and the information content that can be perceived by humans.

AR pursues virtual integration with reality, while VR emphasizes a completely virtual environment. Both AR and VR make use of digital information, but use different interfaces. The two pursue different directions, but there are many overlapping market needs. So, there is a competitive relationship. For example, in the field of education, AR/VR training (according to the data of Internet Data Center, AR/VR training will be worth more than $8 billion by 2023) can not only assist teaching and training with virtual things in reality but also carry out teaching work in a completely virtual environment. This kind of market overlap makes AR/VR enterprises more competitive. The key to market competition is user experience. The most important thing in user experience is the fidelity of the image, the second is the interaction ability, and the last is the requirements on the environment and the impact on human health.

AR/VR technology has been widely used in projects and products in various fields such as medicine, military, design, industry, training, and transportation, among which there are some high-tech and cutting-edge products. In the medical field, AR/VR technology is used to build a virtual mannequin, so as to simulate surgical operation and achieve the purpose of training and learning. Pieper and Satara and others built a virtual surgical trainer based on two SGI workstations in the early 1990s to simulate leg and abdominal surgery.

Today, VR technology can even be used to conduct remotely controlled surgery, and with the information provided by computers, the rate of surgical errors will be greatly reduced. Although AR technology has a high application threshold in the medical field, exploratory teaching, scientific research, and even clinical application have begun to emerge in many disciplines, such as anatomy teaching, simulated surgical training, intraoperative navigation, and rehabilitation training. China has also made great progress in clinical application research and development of AR technology.

For example, in 2017, the Weihai Central Hospital successfully completed the resection of a huge spindle cell tumor and the replacement of artificial vertebral body by utilizing AR technology and 3D printing technology. During the operation, the blood vessel, tissue, and lesion site of the patient were presented to the doctor at a 360° angle of view, which greatly increased the safety of the operation and the accuracy of the operation.

This is the first time for China to combine AR technology with 3D printing technology and apply it to the field of orthopedics. In the surgical environment assisted by AR technology, the visualization effect combined with the accurate medical image and tracking system, aiming, registering, and calculating the information and data of the whole operation will greatly reduce the surgical risk and create a safer surgical environment. With the help of head-worn displays or AR technology, doctors can perform surgery better, help build a more trusting relationship between patients and doctors, and will surely bring profound changes to the medical field in the future (Fig. 4.5).

For the application of AR/VR in the medical field, the resolution and clarity of the picture are very important, which directly affects the accuracy of doctors' judgment while using AR/VR equipment in diagnosis and treatment. Because doctors need to put on the devices near their eyes like glasses when using AR/VR devices, the resolution of the devices will be more stringent. The basic 2K resolution is far from the fine effect doctors need.

However, the network environment created by 5G connection and 5G chip can provide AR/VR medical devices with ultra-clear screen resolution of 4K or even 8K. The advent of the 5G era has greatly improved the connection speed of the LET network, perfectly solved the problems such as interaction delay, frame drop, and lack of fluency in AR/VR diagnosis and treatment and eliminated the sense of vertigo caused by unclear and unfluent pictures.

In the future, for medical students and doctors with junior experience, 5G+AR/VR teaching will be a teaching method with multiple people synchronously, immersive and allowing learners to experience the integration

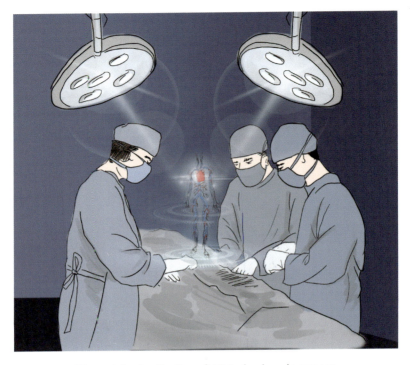

Figure 4.5　Application of AR technology in surgery.

of virtuality and reality. Therefore, this teaching method combining virtuality and reality must be the future development direction of medical education. In the future medical education, teachers will be able to better understand the learning dynamics of medical students through real-time analysis of 5G data and present every medical detail to medical students, so as to reduce their learning burden and improve their learning efficiency. Medical students can also give feedback in a timely manner. In practice, with the help of AR equipment, medical students can see the virtualized practice equipment operated by teachers from different perspectives, which greatly improves learning efficiency and security during practice and reduces equipment expenditure.

In the future, medical students can give full play to their imagination and create more new medical methods through 5G+AR/VR. Even if medical students ask for leave when they are sick, they can learn from 5G+AR/VR through remote interactive learning, anytime and anywhere. For medical schools with poor teaching quality and underdeveloped medical areas, medical teaching communication is difficult and teachers are scarce. 5G+AR/VR can provide high-quality teaching, share famous teachers and share high-quality teaching resources, and make high-quality medical education in underdeveloped medical areas possible.

Therefore, the development of 5G technology and AR/VR technology will greatly change the traditional teaching and communication mode, thus forming a new diversified teaching and communication mode. At the same time, surgeons have a high demand for more visibility during surgery. 5G+AR/VR can help surgeons perform operations with the clearest vision with the least incision exposure and the least harm to the patient. In the future, surgeons could monitor patients' health with real-time imaging and navigation systems.

VR technology and AR technology will advance in an alternate development in the future. In the beginning, VR technology may be popularized in the way of entertainment and drive the development of AR technology. AR technology will catch up and become the mainstream lifestyle. Maybe these two technologies will constantly switch the leading role, but they will also support each other, learn from and merge with each other, and ultimately make a huge difference in people's lives. AR/VR are both the "king" of the new era and will show their unique advantages in medicine. AR/VR and spatial computing have already shown some potential in healthcare applications, and 5G is expected to enhance doctors' ability to innovate and treat patients in a less invasive way.

4.2.2 Machine intelligence: "Iron and steel" doctor would serve you wholeheartedly

In science fiction movies, we often see amazing medical robots. This kind of robot can not only help patients with postoperative rehabilitation exercises but also replace nurses to deliver medicine, deliver laboratory specimens, help transport patients with mobility difficulties, and even perform surgery for patients. Such a multi-functional robot, if it really becomes a reality, will benefit all of mankind, but it will also become a milestone in human development. In recent years, artificial intelligence is upsurging. With the continuous improvement of science and technology, artificial intelligence is gradually becoming a reality in the hands of scientists under the wisdom and rich imagination of human beings and has been widely used in our real life. Since the birth of the surgical robot, the public has paid special attention to it. Businesspeople value its huge commercial value, surgeons value its subversion of the traditional operating system of surgery, and most medical workers value its influence on future medicine.

How to do surgery in the future? Who will do it? In the future, surgical robots are likely to perform surgery on patients. A surgical robot is a medical device product integrating medicine, mechanics, biomechanics, and computer science. The complete surgical robot system is composed of a computer-integrated surgical system and a medical robot, which can provide support for doctors in terms of vision, hearing, and touch for surgical operation, effectively improve the quality of diagnosis and assessment of the patient, target location, precise operation and surgical training of doctors, and shorten the recovery period of patients.

When a surgical robot is used, the doctor's hands do not need to touch the patient. Once the location of the incision is determined, a robotic arm equipped with a camera and other surgical tools will cut, stop the bleeding, and sew up the wound. The surgeon will simply sit on a console and watch and control the arm. The doctor's operation is filtered through a computer system and then scaled to a more detailed operation, which, together with an enlarged 3D HD camera in the field of view, maximizes the abilities of the doctor's hands and eyes. The Daily Mail reported that William Beaver, an assistant vicar at St Mary's Church in Oxford, UK, received a surgical operation conducted by a surgical robot in September 2016.

This 70-year-old suffered from an eye disease that caused a thin film to appear on the surface of his retina, distorting his vision to look like a distorting mirror. Removing this thin film, which is just 0.01 mm thick, without damaging the retina is beyond the doctor's limit. This was when the powerful surgical robot came in. It inserted a thin needle into the eye and successfully stripped away the membrane through a series of operations. Although robots have been used in the developed world before, an operation inside the eye is unprecedented. From this example, we can see the great potential of a surgical robot.

At present, the most famous surgical robot is the da Vinci surgical robot. The da Vinci Surgical System is an advanced robotic platform designed to perform complex surgical procedures using a minimally invasive approach. The da Vinci surgical robot consists of three parts: the surgeon's console, the bedside robotic arm system, and the imaging system.

The da Vinci surgical robot once performed a precise surgical operation. But it wasn't the patient who was operated on. It was a grape. What's even more amazing is that the grape came in a glass bottle. The da Vinci surgical robot stitched the "Skin" of the grape successfully and the precision of the whole process is amazing.

Orthopedic and neurosurgical robots in China are mainly domestic products. Beijing Tianzhihang Medical Technology Co., Ltd., together with Beijing Jishuitan Hospital, Beihang University, and other units, has developed the "TiRobot" orthopedic surgery robot with complete independent intellectual property rights. "TiRobot" is the world's first orthopedic robot that can carry out full-segment surgery, with high surgical accuracy and the world's leading level of indication range and positioning accuracy.

China has made some achievements in the research and development of the surgical robot, but there is still a gap between China and the international leading level, and further technological breakthroughs are needed. It is believed that in the future, with the continuous improvement of China's manufacturing industry, the continuous improvement of the theoretical system of surgical robot technology, the continuous improvement of the efficiency of achievement transformation, and the more diversified ways of capital investment, the surgical robot industry will embrace a golden period of development.

The robots are the tools of doctors, realizing the operability and replicability of doctors' experience and ideas, and 5G is the bridge connecting the two. 5G not only connects people but also shortens the distance between people and things. The popularization of 5G will profoundly change the traditional medical model. In the future, through 5G remote health monitoring data, we can use professional equipment, such as electrocardiograph, ventilator, and sphygmomanometer, for continuous, real-time and long-term monitoring of heart rate, blood sugar, blood pressure, blood oxygen, and other health indicators of patients, and they would send back data to the medical staff through the 5G cloud, so that the medical staff can obtain the patient's vital sign data in time.

This scenario breaks the traditional medical model. 5G background can timely analyze data, pre-judge critical values, and report to medical workers, which is conducive to the judgment of patients' condition. In the past, many chronic and malignant diseases could no longer be cured by doctors when they were diagnosed. In the future, with the help of the 5G network, "early detection, early diagnosis and early treatment" could be truly realized, so as to avoid the huge burden brought to patients' families by diseases. With the help of the 5G network, life science will develop toward mastering personal health information and monitoring personal health data.

Although surgical robots have emerged in the field of surgery, surgical robots are still inseparable from the operation and monitoring of surgeons, and the mismatch between network speed and surgical requirements has also become one of the potential risks. The advent of the 5G era will provide ultra-low response delay and provide hardware guarantee for surgeons to operate surgical robots. 5G boasts unique network advantages such as high speed, low time delay, wide connection, deep connection of things, and high-security performance, which can greatly overcome various outstanding problems under the previous 4G network conditions.

Even the doctors on the far side can also realize real-time monitoring data sharing, two-way transmission of control signals, and real-time interaction of high-definition audio and video under the guarantee of 5G network to monitor patients' data in real time, understand real-time scenes, and complete remote operation of surgery. All these have made great grassroots medical institutions for the patients. China's 5G industry has been booming, but it still faces many serious problems in the development process.

5G networks will push the smart medical industry toward faster lifesaving, more balanced allocation of medical resources, and more timely monitoring of patients' conditions and contribute to the national health management. The establishment of a wide-connected 5G network is the foundation for the development of WIT120. Hospitals, doctors, and universities should proceed from the most real needs of patients, promote the in-depth integration of industry, universities, and research institutes, and constantly explore ways to combine 5G technology with surgical robots and 5G intelligent medical application scenarios that are easy to promote, so that 5G technology can be implemented in the field of healthcare and ultimately benefit the general public.

4.3 Relevant Laws and Regulations

4.3.1 *Will privacy breaches happen in medical data?*

The application and popularization of 5G have brought tremendous changes to the field of information data, but the increase in data transmission volume also brings greater risks to the security of data transmission. Although 5G technology combines multimedia communication and web services and real-time media streaming with the aid of ICN (information-centric networking). It takes information as the center, realizes the functions of information search, transmission and distribution, solves the problems existing in the traditional IP, and improves the security of data transmission to a certain extent. But no one can claim that 5G is 100% safe. Consider medical data as an example, when medical data leaks and citizens' privacy rights are violated, how should they be held accountable? What are the relevant laws and regulations (Fig. 4.6)?

In legal liability issues of acquisition and application of healthcare data, healthcare-specific laws, regulations, and operational rules on healthcare Big Data are not yet complete. Although there are a number of policy documents as guidelines, including the Opinions of the General Office of the State Council on Promoting the Development of "Internet+ Medical and Health" and the Notice on Printing and Issuing the Administrative Measures for Internet Diagnosis and Treatment (Trial), the implementation and promotion of the specific system still need to be promulgated and implemented by the relevant competent departments.

This situation inevitably led to the dilemma of "having no law to abide" for the market in the process of mining and application of healthcare Big Data, and we can only "across the river by feeling the stones", which to a certain extent, inhibits the research in relevant fields and the

Figure 4.6   Legal liability in WIT120.

vitality of the WIT120 market. At present, there are several risks in the application of healthcare Big Data: (1) the risk of privacy leakage of medical data; (2) uncertainty risks of attribution of Big Data healthcare.

In the *Management Measures on the Standards, Safety and Service of the National Health Care Data (For Trial Implementation)* released on the website of the National Health Committee in September 2018, the concept of healthcare Big Data was clarified for the first time. Healthcare Big Data refers to the data related to healthcare generated in the process of disease prevention and treatment and health management. The *Management Measures* mainly defines the regulatory units and responsibility units of healthcare Big Data and standardize the healthcare Big Data from the aspects of standard management, safety management, service management, etc.

For the risk of privacy disclosure of medical data, the legal issues involved mainly include four aspects:

(1) *Legal collection of healthcare Big Data*: In the process of collecting and acquiring health and medical Big Data, according to the provisions of the *Cybersecurity Law of the People's Republic of China*, "Data collection shall follow the principles of legality, propriety and necessity. Make public the rules of collection and use, clearly state the purpose, method and scope of information collection and use, and obtain the consent of the collected". For the part of the original personal information, "Collectors shall not collect personal information irrelevant to the services they provide, and shall not collect and use personal information in violation of the provisions of laws, administrative regulations and the agreement of both parties".

However, at present, there is still controversy whether the healthcare data derived from disease diagnosis and treatment, health examination conducted by medical institutions, and physical examination centers belong to the individual patient or to the corresponding medical service units. This also leads to the grey area in the acquisition and use of healthcare data involved in the above dispute, which lays out the risk and hidden danger of incomplete laws for the subsequent development and application of healthcare Big Data.

In this regard, in the collection process of healthcare Big Data, it is necessary to go through legal and formal procedures, obtain effective authorization from relevant units and individuals of health and medical Big Data in an all-round way, and at the same time do a good job in relevant laws and regulation constraints and standardized management of data collection.

(2) *Storage and protection of healthcare Big Data*: The *Management Measures on the Standards, Safety and Service of the National Health Care Data (For Trial Implementation)* clearly put forward the requirements, "The responsible units shall have the data storage, disaster recovery backup and safety management conditions that meet the relevant requirements of the state, and strengthen the storage management of healthcare big data". "Responsible units shall, in accordance with the requirements of the state network security protection system, build reliable network security environment, strengthen the construction of security guarantee system for related systems of healthcare big data, improve the safety protection ability for key information infrastructure and the important information system, to ensure the security and control of key information infrastructure and core system of healthcare big data. Healthcare big data centers for and relevant information systems should all carry out grading, filing and evaluation".

In fact, long before the proposal of the bill, the legal department had placed the personal information of citizens in an important position. The law regarded the Big Data of medical records as the common property between the medical record holders and the patients, so that it can be said that there is no more strict law on privacy protection than this. But considering that late-stage development and application of the healthcare Big Data requires the authorization and agreement of the parties concerned, if the patient's private information is not protected, then the patient's trust will be lost. Therefore, it is suggested that relevant medical institutions strictly implement the storage and protection security level requirements for healthcare Big Data and focus on the protection of patient privacy.

(3) *The application of Big Data in healthcare*: As for the application of health and medical Big Data, Article 42 of the *Cybersecurity Law of the People's Republic of China* stipulates, "Network operators shall not disclose, alter or damage the personal information they have collected; Personal information shall not be provided to others without the consent of the collected person. Except for those that have been processed and cannot be identified by a particular individual and cannot be recovered".

It can be seen that after legal collection, standardization, and desensitization of healthcare Big Data, it can be used legally without the consent of the collected person. This effectively reduces the legal barriers to the practical application of healthcare Big Data and provides strong institutional protection for the mining, analysis, and application research and development of healthcare Big Data. The *Cybersecurity Law of the People's Republic of China* has left a lot of space for further mining, analysis, and application of health and medical Big Data. However, in the process of external use of health and medical Big Data, all medical units should abide by various policies and provisions to avoid violating the law.

(4) *Overseas transmission of health and medical Big Data*: In May 2014, the National Health and Family Planning Commission (NHFPC) stipulated in the *Administration of Population Health Information (for Trial Implementation)* that "Population health information shall not be stored in overseas servers, and overseas servers shall not be hosted or rented". With the changes in the industry structure and actual development needs of multinational companies in the field of healthcare Big Data in practice, this decree has been correspondingly broadened.

But according to the *Guidelines for Information Security Technology Data Exit Security Assessment (Consultation Paper)* released in August 2017, the National Information Security Standardization Technical Committee clearly stipulates that "population health" and "food and drugs" are included in important data fields and that the exit of personal information and important data is restricted. Other detailed evaluation criteria are also set. For the current exit of health and medical Big Data, relevant medical units should judge and make a preliminary assessment of their own situation according to the *Guidelines for Information Security Technology Data Exit Security Assessment (Consultation Paper)*, so as to prepare for the subsequent possible exit evaluation requirements of healthcare Big Data.

4.3.2 Who is responsible for WIT120?

WIT120 is one of the important fields in the highly developed application of 5G technology. It aims to develop intelligent terminals with the advantages of Big Data and Internet of Things brought by 5G technology and to establish a new medical interaction mode based on artificial intelligence. For the uncertain risk of imputation of WIT120, it is mainly the corresponding legal challenge faced by the clinical application of medical artificial intelligence, such as the dispute of the corresponding responsibility assumed by the resident doctors and the attribution of liability of data terminal.

The attribution of responsibility for Big Data medical services mainly refers to the problem of who bears the main responsibility for the patients' physical abnormalities after receiving Big Data medical services. The subjects involved mainly include developers of Big Data algorithms, manufacturers of products, and medical staff who purchase instruments. Under the current legal system, the legal personality regulation of artificial intelligence, especially medical artificial intelligence, is still absent, and the legal status and specific norms of artificial intelligence need to be clarified urgently.

The application of medical artificial intelligence based on 5G and Big Data technology in the fields of diagnosis, treatment, nursing, and health management shows a trend of gradual expansion and deepening. Considering its development potential and relevant medical application prospects, the law should encourage the development of this innovative technology. However, with the continuous application of medical artificial intelligence in clinical practice, legal liability issues and disputes are inevitable. Who shall be the resident doctor? Can a data terminal take responsibility for a medical error? Such questions may inevitably arise in the minds of the patients. In addition, whether patients can accept the medical risks caused by individual particularity in medical services based on Big Data is also an urgent issue to be solved in the development of medical services based on Big Data.

Who shall be the resident doctor? It depends on whether the legal identity of medical AI can be legally defined. When medical artificial intelligence is used in diagnosis, treatment, and nursing, it has not been confirmed by law whether the actor is a medical device or a doctor. In addition, the admission standards of doctors and medical artificial intelligence are not consistent, and relevant laws need to be improved to define whether doctors operate devices or independent medical artificial intelligence.

Can the data terminal take responsibility? Artificial diagnosis and treatment will inevitably make mistakes. While 5G, Big Data, and artificial intelligence technologies are statistically accurate, their own development and application results are uncertain, which may lead to uncontrollable or unpredictable risks. It is difficult to avoid the phenomenon of medical artificial intelligence misdiagnosis or operation error. When a patient is harmed, is the legal liability for AI itself, or the medical institution and its personnel, or the developers and manufacturers of medical AI, or even the technical support parties of 5G, artificial intelligence, and Big Data technologies? This problem needs to be solved urgently.

As early as 1972, people began to try to apply artificial intelligence in the medical field. The successful development of the MYCIN system is one of the examples. In the 1990s, the application of computer-aided diagnosis and other technologies was continuously developed. In 2015, Watson developed by IBM gained worldwide attention for its deep learning to treat a variety of cancers, including lung cancer and prostate cancer.

In 2017, the *Development Plan on the New Generation of Artificial Intelligence* issued by the State Council proposed to explore the construction of smart hospitals, promote the application of new models and methods of artificial intelligence treatment, and establish a fast and accurate intelligent medical system. Domestic artificial intelligence medical projects have been springing up ever since. For example, Tencent's "Miying" esophageal cancer early screening system was applied in Guangxi Zhuang Autonomous Region People's Hospital. Ali Health has launched Doctor You, a medical artificial intelligence system, providing medical image detection, doctor training, and other services. There are also several da Vinci surgical robots stationed in hospitals in China.

The da Vinci surgical robot is already excellent, but there are still safety risks. During Britain's first heart valve repair operation operated by a da Vinci robot in 2015, the robot's robotic arm suddenly went awry, slapping the doctor's hand and even putting the patient's heart in the wrong place during the operation, resulting in a puncture in the main artery of the patient. More seriously, because the machine replaced the manual operation, the doctor cannot perceive the patient's physical condition during the operation in real time and cannot timely adjust the operation plan according to the clinical manifestations. Therefore, once hardware defects or program vulnerabilities occur in the process of surgery, nursing, and examination, artificial intelligence is likely to cause medical accidents (Fig. 4.7).

Watson is an outstanding example of a cognitive computing system and a technology platform. But Watson, with its features of "technology black box" and "self-learning", fails to explain the reasoning behind its

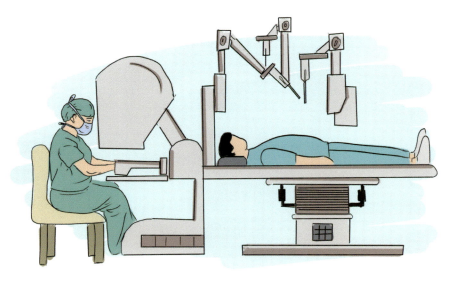

Figure 4.7　Surgical robot.

decisions, its algorithms, and why treatments are given to specific patients. Sometimes, even the clinicians may doubt the proposition it proposed. In this case, what is the legal liability of a doctor who adopts or fails to adopt Watson's scheme and thus causes a misdiagnosis? The safety standard of artificial intelligence for this kind of surgery has not been finalized, so it can be seen that once a medical accident occurs, it is not clear who is responsible, and relevant laws and regulations still need to be improved.

At present, China's relevant regulatory authorities are very strict in the examination and verification of diagnosis by using artificial intelligence technology. Relevant laws and regulations, such as the new edition of *Medical Device Classification Catalogue* issued by the National Medical Products Administration in 2017, also strictly classify artificial intelligence. There is still a big gap between the advanced artificial intelligence and our current technology development depth. The Big Data medical care stipulated in the established Big Data medical risk prevention and control methods is still limited to the shallow and primary intelligence level. Legal standards and industry norms have not been defined for the application of completely independent thinking autonomous AI in clinical diagnosis and treatment.

To sum up, due to the imperfection and the lag of laws and regulations system, the legal system of the Big Data health industry has not yet been fully established. In the process of applying medical Big Data derived from 5G technology and derivatives based on Big Data, such as artificial intelligence and other products, all medical units still need to adhere to the principle of prudent, strict, and reasonable utilization and standardize the application of the system products.

Bibliography

An Zhiping, Gao Zhijun, Zhang Yunhong *et al*. (2016). Application and construction of remote information query system for medical records. *Journal of Medical Postgraduates* 29 (12): 1325–1327.

Chen Jiahe, Ma Jinlu, and Zhang Yuwei (2020). Research on the influencing factors of patients' willingness to continue online consultation and offline medical treatment under Internet medical care. *Chinese General Practice* (25): 3164–3169.

Cui Hongen, Zhang Chao, and Xia Yan (2019). Heart rate evaluation based on wearable smart bracelet. *Measurement Devices and Applications* 29 (6): 26–31.

Du Xiaoming and Li Yiming (2019). 5G Promoting the leap-forward development of smart medical care. *C-Enterprise Management* (10): 42–45.

Ge Yanli, Wang Zhirong, and Yang Changqing (2018). Medical students' ability to communicate between doctors and patients in the current medical environment. *Health Vocational Education* 36 (11): 17–18.

Guo Xiaoya (2018). Peking University Oncology online Cloud Medical Records. *China Hospital CEO* (17): 80–81.

He Min (2006). Speed up the development of rural and community medical services to help poor people in urban and rural areas get medical treatment. *Democracy Monthly* (05): 1.

Heng Fanxiu (2018). Personal health records (PHR) are now available. *Popular Science* (05): 24.

Huang Su (2016). Sichuan Mobile builds "Internet + medical treatment" online and offline to solve the difficulty of medical treatment. *Communications & Information Technology* (03): 49.

Li Junhuai, Zhou Mingquan, and Geng Guohua (2002). Current situation and prospect of telemedicine at home and abroad. *International Journal of Biomedical Engineering* (05): 193–195, 202.

Li Xiaodong, Lin Xiaoyi, and Chen Junjian (2019). Design and implementation of online and offline comprehensive health service platform. *Technology Innovation Application* (10): 25–27.

Liu Xiang, Zhu Shijun, and Li Xinchun (2004). The current situation, difficulties and countermeasures of telemedicine development in China. *Chinese Hospitals* 8 (6): 8–11.

Liu Xin (2006). Medical dispute caused by communication barriers in nurses and patients. *China Nursing Management* (07): 19–20.

Luo Jianping (2006). Analysis of physical and mental health status and medical treatment problems of entitled groups in rural areas // Rehabilitation Medicine Working Committee of China Association of Social Workers. Compilation of the Ninth National Psychiatric Academic Conference 2006. Beijing: 199–200.

Mou Lan and Jin Xinxin (2012). A review of the development of telemedicine. *Soft Science of Health* 26 (06): 506–509.

Pantelopoulos, A. and Bourbakis, N. G. (2010). A survey on wearable sensor-based systems for health monitoring and prognosis. *IEEE Transactions on Systems Man & Cybernetics Part C* 40(1): 1–12.

Shi Xujian (2019). 5G: Forget about Technology, let's talk about demand. *Big Data Time* (10): 40–47.

Sun Xiuwei and Yan Li, Li Yanfeng, 2007. The application of virtual virtual reality technology in medical treatment. *Healthcare Devices* (5): 17–20.

Tang Chao (2017). When VR technology meets medical care. *China Hospital CEO* (2): 86.

Tian Xin (2006). Working hard to solve the difficulties people face in accessing medical services and building a harmonious relationship between doctors and patients. *Chinese Hospital* (11): 72–73.

Wang Jianping, Tang Zhe, Sun Fei, *et al.* (2012). Analysis of the related factors of medical difficulties in elderly people in Beijing. *Chinese Hospitals* 16 (12): 26–28.

Chunhui Wen (2018). The combination of online and offline services and the coexistence of management services – Smart medical services in Jialong property management. *Urban Development* (05): 72–73.

Wen Jun (2018). Strengthen communication between doctors and patients and improve their relationship. *World Latest Medicine Information* 18 (49): 196.

Wu Jianxiong (2016). A Platform for Remote Medical Health Consultation and Management: CN106096280A. 2016-11-09.

Wu Lin and Liu Guiyun (2019). How could medical staff effectively communicate with medical rescuers. *China Economist* 08: 273.

Wu Qiong and Chen Min (2013). The system architecture and key technologies of WIT120. *China Digital Medicine* 8 (08): 98–100.

Xie Junxiang and Zhang Lin (2016). The development of WIT120. *China Medical Device Information* 22 (11): 11–16.
Yang Binglei, Yang Xiaodan, Xu Lingling, *et al*. (2018). Health management system based on WeChat. *Internet of Things Technologies* 8 (04): 49–50, 53.
Yang Hui, Xue Song, Gu Guangli, *et al*. (2017). Retrieval system for similar medical records based on medical big data platform. *Military Medical Journal of Southeast China* 19 (02): 210–212.
Zhao Jie (2019). Application and construction strategy of WIT120. *Electronic Technology and Software Engineering* (22): 256–257.
Zhao Yijun and Zhang Tao (2015). Analysis of the current situation of the development of smart wearable devices in the field of health. *Chinese Journal of Health Informatics & Management* (4): 354–358.
Zhong Qiyan (2019). Investigation and analysis of privacy protection of personal electronic health records in China: An investigation and analysis from the perspective of the general public. *Archives Science Study* (06): 66–71.
Zhou Dengfeng, He Zhen, Shao Zhuangchao, *et al*. (2016). Current situation and development of network medical design. *Hospital Administration Journal of Chinese People's Liberation Army* 23 (02): 192–194.
Zhou Wei, Dong Qing, Zhou Zuojian, *et al*. (2015). Architecture design for health management information platform based on intelligent terminal device. *Chinese Journal of Health Informatics and Management* 12 (1): 49–54.
Zhou Yun and Li Weimin (2019). Discussion on the transformation trend of medical service model in 5G era. *West China Medical Journal* (12): 1–4.

Index

5G, v–vii, ix–xi, xiii–xv, 11, 14, 20–21, 24, 30–40, 48–49, 53–54, 56–59, 61–62, 64–71, 73–74, 76, 78, 80–81, 84–85, 88–89, 91–93, 95–97, 100–102, 104
5G ambulance, 68
5G cloud medical records, 41–46
5G mobile medical care, 39–40
5G remote full outpatient, 37
5G remote surgery, 37–39
5G telemedicine training, 40–41
5G+ AI Diagnosis, 74–78

A
ambulance, 67–69
AR/VR applications driven by 5G, 69–70

B
Big Data, 11–12, 14, 22, 28, 30–32, 36, 45, 48, 56, 58, 61–64, 66–67, 75, 84–89, 97–104

H
holographic projection, 81–85

I
intelligent blood pressure monitor, 67
intelligent hospital guidance robot, 32–33
intelligent medicine box, 65–66
intelligent terminal, 26, 61–62, 65–66, 100
Internet medical services, 7–8, 31

M
management of personal health records, 49–53
medical cloud, 87
medical Internet of Things, 48, 87
mobile medical library, 14–16, 24, 29–30

P
personalized medical care, 46–49

R
remote diagnosis, 35–36
remote monitoring, 53–56
remote surgery, 35, 73

S
smart bracelet, 62–65
smart health management, 15–16, 24, 28–29
smart outpatient service, 14–15, 24–26
smart ward, 14–15, 24, 26–28
smart watch, 62–65
surgical robot, 38, 94–96, 102

V
virtual teaching platform based on augmented reality (AR)/virtual reality (VR), 70–73
VR ward visits, 73

W
WIT120, 10–24, 30, 32, 48, 96–98, 100–104